Your Personal Stress Profile and Activity Workbook

Jerrold S. Greenberg

Book Team
Editor *Chris Rogers*
Production Coordinator *Peggy Selle*

Wm. C. Brown Publishers
President *G. Franklin Lewis*
Vice President, Publisher *George Wm. Bergquist*
Vice President, Publisher *Thomas E. Doran*
Vice President, Operations and Production *Beverly Kolz*
National Sales Manager *Virginia S. Moffat*
Senior Marketing Manager *Kathy Law Laube*
Marketing Manager *George H. Chapin*
Executive Editor *Edgar J. Laube*
Managing Editor, Production *Colleen A. Yonda*
Production Editorial Manager *Julie A. Kennedy*
Production Editorial Manager *Ann Fuerste*
Publishing Services Manager *Karen J. Slaght*
Manager of Visuals and Design *Faye M. Schilling*

WCB Group
President-Chief Executive Officer *Mark C. Falb*
Chairman of the Board *Wm. C. Brown*

Cover design and photo by Morris Lundin

ISBN 0-697-14109-8

Printed in the United States of America by Wm. C. Brown Publishers, 2460 Kerper Boulevard, Dubuque, IA 52001

10 9 8 7 6 5 4 3 2 1

TABLE OF CONTENTS

	Preface	vii
Section I:	**Using Stress Management Techniques**	1
	1) Introduction: How Often Do You Use Techniques That Are Helpful in Managing Stress?	1
	Scale: Stress Management Checklist	3
	Scoring	5
	Interpretation of Scores	5
	Activity	7
Section II:	**Avoiding Life Stress**	9
	1) Introduction: How Often Do You Have Feelings That Are Generally Associated with Stress?	9
	Scale: Stress Log	11
	Scoring	12
	Interpretation of Scores	12
	2) Introduction: Are You Avoiding Stress or Experiencing Significant Distress?	13
	Scale: Psychological Health	13
	Scoring	15
	Interpretation of Scores	15
	3) Introduction: Are You Experiencing Excessive Anxiety or Depression?	17
	Scale: Personal Feelings Inventory	17
	Scoring	20
	Interpretation of Scores	20
	Activity	21
Section III:	**Life Satisfaction**	25
	1) Introduction: How Satisfied Are You with Your Overall Life?	25
	Scale: Life Satisfaction Inventory	27

	Scoring	28
	Interpretation of Scores	28
	2) Introduction: How Satisfied Are You with Particular Facets of Your Life?	29
	Scale: NIDA Life Satisfaction Questionnaire	29
	Scoring	34
	Interpretation of Scores	34
	Activity	35
Section IV:	**Stress Knowledge**	37
	1) Introduction: How Much Do You Know About Stress and Its Effects?	37
	Scale: Facts about Stress	39
	Scoring	40
	Interpretation of Scores	40
	2) Introduction: How Much Do You Know About How to Manage Stress Effectively?	41
	Scale: Coping with Stress	41
	Scoring	43
	Interpretation of Scores	43
	Activity	44
Section V:	**Techniques for Responding Appropriately to Stress**	49
	1) Introduction: How Effective Would You Be in Responding to Stressful Situations?	49
	Scale: Appropriate Responses to Stress	51
	Scoring	54
	Interpretation of Scores	55
	Activity	57
Section VI:	**Using Systematic Decision-Making Skills**	59
	1) Introduction: What Do You Know About Systematic Decision Making?	59
	Scale: Decision Making	61
	Scoring	66
	Interpretation of Scores	67

2) Introduction: How Valuable Do You Believe Systematic Decision Making Is In Arriving at Appropriate Decisions? 69
Scale: Ideas about Systematic Decision Making 69
Scoring 71
Interpretation of Scores 71

3) Introduction: How Strong Is Your Intention to Use Systematic Decision-Making Skills? 73
Scale: Would You Use Systematic Decision Making? 73
Scoring 75
Interpretation of Scores 75
Activity 77

Section VII: Effective Communication Techniques 79

1) Introduction: How Well Can You Communicate Your Feelings of Stress to Other People? 79
Scale: Communicating about Stress 81
Scoring 85
Interpretation of Scores 85

2) Introduction: How Well Can You Communicate Acceptance and Understanding When Other People Share Their Stressful Feelings with You? 87
Scale: Responding to Others about Stress 87
Scoring 91
Interpretation of Scores 92
Activity 93

Section VIII: Positive Outlook on Life 97

1) Introduction: How Optimistic Are You About Your Future? 97
Scale: How Will You Feel? 99
Scoring 100
Interpretation of Scores 101
Activity 102

Section IX: Intention to Use Stress Management Techniques 107

1) Introduction: How Effective Do You Think You Can Be In Managing Stress? 107
Scale: Keeping Your Cool 109
Scoring 112
Interpretation of Scores 112

2) Introduction: How Intent Are You on Using Stress Management Techniques? 113
Scale: Will You Manage Stress? 113
Scoring 115
Interpretation of Scores 116
Activity 117

PREFACE

This book is designed to meet two basic purposes. First, it will allow you to evaluate yourself relative to stress. That is, you will develop a personal stress profile based on your responses to seventeen stress-related scales. These scales were either developed for and/or appear in *An Evaluation Handbook for Health Education Programs in Stress Management** published by the Centers for Disease Control of the United States government. This stress profile will include the following components:

1. Your use of effective stress management techniques.
2. How well you avoid stress and accompanying feelings.
3. How satisfied you are with your life.
4. How much you know about stress.
5. Your ability to use effective stress management techniques.
6. Your ability to employ systematic decision-making skills.
7. Your skills in communicating about stress.
8. Your outlook on life.
9. Your intention to use stress management techniques.

Second, instructional activities are presented to teach you stress management knowledge and skills. These activities require you be an active participant rather than merely reading about stress and stress management.

The intent, then, is to relate stress to you *personally* and to help you acquire skills to better manage the stress of your life. Without any further ado, let's proceed to actually do that.

---

*Centers for Disease Control. *An Evaluation Handbook for Health Education Programs in Stress Management.* Washington, D.C.: Department of Health and Human Services, 1983.

Section I

Using Stress Management Techniques

One way to prevent stress from leading to negative consequences—be they ill health, poor relationships, poor job performance, or low grades in school—is to employ a variety of stress management techniques and strategies. This section speaks to your use of stress management techniques.

1) INTRODUCTION

How Often Do You Use Techniques That Are Helpful in Managing Stress?

There are a number of techniques that have been shown to be effective in managing stress. The following scale measures how often you use such techniques.

SCALE: STRESS MANAGEMENT CHECKLIST

Listed below are things that people sometimes do to manage stress. Think back over the past *month.* Place a check (✓) to show how often, during the past month, you have done each thing.

During the past month, how often did you . . .	REGULARLY	OCCASIONALLY	RARELY
1. . . . get plenty of rest at night?	____	____	____
2. . . . talk about your feelings with friends or family members?	____	____	____
3. . . . take breaks when doing difficult tasks?	____	____	____
4. . . . drink *less* than three cups of coffee per day?	____	____	____
5. . . . plan your time so that you could meet all your responsibilities?	____	____	____
6. . . . use relaxation techniques?	____	____	____
7. . . . ask others for help when you felt you had too much to do?	____	____	____
8. . . . exercise?	____	____	____

	REGULARLY	OCCASIONALLY	RARELY
9. . . . talk about your problems with the people who were involved in them?	_____	_____	_____
10. . . . figure out whether or not you were feeling stress?	_____	_____	_____
11. . . . find interesting things to do when you were bored?	_____	_____	_____
12. . . . plan time for relaxation?	_____	_____	_____
13. . . . look at the positive things in your life?	_____	_____	_____
14. . . . say "no" to helping others when you felt you already had enough to do?	_____	_____	_____
15. . . . set realistic goals for yourself?	_____	_____	_____

Source: Centers for Disease Control. *An Evaluation Handbook for Health Education Programs in Stress Management.* Washington, D.C.: Department of Health and Human Services, 1983, pp. 76–79.

SCORING

Assign the following point values for each response:

Regularly	=	3
Occasionally	=	2
Rarely	=	1

Next, add the points and divide by 15.

INTERPRETATION OF SCORES

This is a scale that measures your use of a variety of stress management techniques. The maximum score obtainable of 3 indicates you frequently use a variety of stress management techniques, a score of 2 indicates you occasionally use stress management techniques, and a score of 1 indicates you rarely use stress management techniques. Any score below 2 means you need to employ methods to manage stress on a more regular basis.

ACTIVITY

The *Stress Management Checklist* you just completed includes numerous ways that have been found effective in managing stress. Review this list and identify those which you think have the most relevance to you. That is, which of these techniques do you think are feasible for you to employ given your lifestyle, interests, and needs? Now place that list aside for the meantime. You will come back to it shortly.

There are many other ways that people have found to manage stress. So as not to be limited in your options, interview at least three other people who, in your opinion, seem to have the stress of their lives under control. Ask them the following questions:

1. How do you manage the stress you experience?
2. What do you do to relax?
3. How do you look at stressful events so as to make them less stressful?
4. Who helps you manage the stress of your life?
5. Knowing me, what do you suggest I do to manage the stress that I experience?

From the answers you obtain to these questions, add to your list of stress management strategies. Now that your list is more complete, choose several (at least three) stress management techniques you will try. Remember that you are not wedded to any particular technique. If it is not working, try another. With some effort you will be able to manage the stress of your life. Don't give up.

Which three techniques will you try first?

1. ______________________________

2. ______________________________

3. ______________________________

Section II

Avoiding Life Stress

The degree to which you need to be concerned about stress relates to the amount of stress you experience. This section speaks to the stress in your life and your feelings toward that stress.

1) INTRODUCTION

How Often Do You Have Feelings That Are Generally Associated with Stress?

Having stressful feelings can be quite disturbing. This scale measures the extent to which you experience such feelings. The following scales will measure how well you avoid stress and, in particular, the feelings of anxiety and depression.

SCALE: STRESS LOG

Listed below are descriptions of ways people sometimes feel. Think back over the past *month.* Place a check (✓) to show how often, during the past month, you have felt each way.

During the past month, how often did you feel . . .	REGULARLY	OCCASIONALLY	RARELY
1. . . . that you could not deal with your life?	_____	_____	_____
2. . . . lonely?	_____	_____	_____
3. . . . annoyed by very loud noises?	_____	_____	_____
4. . . . that you had more things to do than you could handle?	_____	_____	_____
5. . . . that nobody really understood you?	_____	_____	_____
6. . . . nervous in a crowded place?	_____	_____	_____
7. . . . that you had no time to relax?	_____	_____	_____
8. . . . that you had no control of your life?	_____	_____	_____
9. . . . that too many things in your life were changing at one time?	_____	_____	_____
10. . . . worthless?	_____	_____	_____
11. . . . that people expected too much from you?	_____	_____	_____

	REGULARLY	OCCASIONALLY	RARELY
12. . . . sad and dis-appointed with life?	_____	_____	_____
13. . . . that you could not do what you wanted to do?	_____	_____	_____
14. . . . that the things you had to do were too hard?	_____	_____	_____
15. . . . that all your work had to be finished at the same time?	_____	_____	_____

SCORING

Assign the following point values for each response:

Regularly	=	3
Occasionally	=	2
Rarely	=	1

Next, add the points and divide by 15.

INTERPRETATION OF SCORES

This is a scale that measures the degree to which you have stressful feelings. The maximum score obtainable of 3 indicates you frequently have feelings associated with stress, a score of 2 indicates you have feelings associated with stress only occasionally, and a score of 1 indicates you rarely have feelings typically associated with stress. Any score above 2 means you experience stressful feelings frequently enough to begin a conscientious program of stress management.

Source: Centers for Disease Control. *An Evaluation Handbook for Health Education Programs in Stress Management.* Washington, D.C.: Department of Health and Human Services, 1983, pp. 69–72.

2) INTRODUCTION

Are You Avoiding Stress or Experiencing Significant Distress?

The extent to which you avoid common problems and complaints contributes to your ability to manage stress. This scale measures the degree to which you avoid such problems and complaints.

SCALE: PSYCHOLOGICAL HEALTH

Below is a list of problems and complaints that people sometimes have. Read each one carefully. INDICATE HOW MUCH THAT PROBLEM HAS BOTHERED OR DISTRESSED YOU DURING THE PAST WEEK INCLUDING TODAY. Circle one answer for each problem. Use the following scale:

HOW MUCH WERE YOU BOTHERED BY:	Not at all	A Little bit	Moder-ately	Quite a bit	Extremely
1. Nervousness or shakiness inside	1	2	3	4	5
2. The idea that someone else can control your thoughts	1	2	3	4	5
3. Feeling others are to blame for most of your troubles	1	2	3	4	5
4. Thoughts of ending your life	1	2	3	4	5
5. Hearing voices that other people do not hear	1	2	3	4	5
6. Suddenly scared for no reason	1	2	3	4	5

	Not at all	A Little bit	Moderately	Quite a bit	Extremely
7. Temper outbursts that you could not control	1	2	3	4	5
8. Feeling blue	1	2	3	4	5
9. Feeling that people are unfriendly or dislike you	1	2	3	4	5
10. Having to check and double-check what you do	1	2	3	4	5
11. Difficulty making decisions	1	2	3	4	5
12. Feeling hopeless about the future	1	2	3	4	5
13. Feeling tense or keyed up	1	2	3	4	5
14. Feeling uneasy when people are watching or talking about you	1	2	3	4	5
15. Having urges to beat, injure, or harm someone	1	2	3	4	5
16. Having urges to break or smash things	1	2	3	4	5
17. Feeling very self-conscious with others	1	2	3	4	5
18. Spells of terror or panic	1	2	3	4	5
19. Feelings of worthlessness	1	2	3	4	5
20. Feeling most people will take advantage of you if you let them	1	2	3	4	5

Source: U.S. Department of Health and Human Services and National Institute on Drug Abuse. *Research Issue 28, Assessing Marijuana Consequences: Selected Questionnaire Items.* (DHHS Publication No. (ADM) 81-1150). Washington, D.C.: U.S. Government Printing Office, 1981.

SCORING

Add up all the answers you circled and divide that sum by 20.

INTERPRETATION OF SCORES

This is a scale that measures whether you are avoiding stress as indicated by the absence of common problems and complaints. The average score on this scale is 7.64. If you scored higher than that, you experience enough problems and complaints to indicate a high level of distress. If you scored lower than 7.64, you experience a manageable level of life stress. However, scores between 6.30 and 9.22 are still within the average range and do not necessitate any changes to manage the stress in your life.

3) INTRODUCTION

Are You Experiencing Excessive Anxiety or Depression?

Two feelings particularly associated with stress are anxiety and depression. This scale measures these feelings and helps you see how stress is manifested in anxious and/or depressed feelings.

SCALE: PERSONAL FEELINGS INVENTORY (PFI)

Please answer these items as they pertain to you now, True or False.

TRUE	FALSE		
____	____	1.	I have less interest than usual in things.
____	____	2.	I have difficulty concentrating.
____	____	3.	I am often sad or depressed.
____	____	4.	I have been uneasy or anxious in the past month.
____	____	5.	I feel depressed most of the time.
____	____	6.	I have trouble giving attention to ordinary routine.
____	____	7.	I have tried to avoid one or more situations in the past month.
____	____	8.	I have felt life wasn't worth living.
____	____	9.	I tremble; my hands are shaky; I feel weak at the knees.
____	____	10.	I have difficulty coming to a conclusion or decision.
____	____	11.	I feel overwhelmed with life.
____	____	12.	My thoughts dwell on a few troubles.
____	____	13.	My hands are sweating and clammy.
____	____	14.	I have kept up very few interests.
____	____	15.	Little if anything interests me.
____	____	16.	I feel hot and cold, and blush or get pale readily.

TRUE	FALSE		
______	______	17.	I spend less time at usual recreational activities.
______	______	18.	I have butterflies or a sinking feeling in my stomach.
______	______	19.	I feel miserable or unhappy.
______	______	20.	I can't concentrate when reading.
______	______	21.	I am bothered by feelings of inadequacy.
______	______	22.	My heart pounds or flutters when I am uneasy or panicky.
______	______	23.	I have too little energy.
______	______	24.	I can't concentrate on movies or T.V. programs.
______	______	25.	I have fear of a particular object or situation.
______	______	26.	I tend to depreciate or criticize myself.
______	______	27.	I have dry or coated mouth.
______	______	28.	I don't seem to smile anymore.
______	______	29.	I enjoy almost nothing.
______	______	30.	I enjoy doing little if anything.
______	______	31.	My fears prevent me from participating in some activities.
______	______	32.	I have had difficulty with my memory lately.
______	______	33.	I keep losing my train of thought.
______	______	34.	I have dizziness, faintness, and/or giddiness.
______	______	35.	I think about my death.
______	______	36.	I have difficulty in getting my breath, and have a choking, tightness in my chest.
______	______	37.	My thoughts get muddled.
______	______	38.	I have trouble remembering something I have just read or heard.
______	______	39.	I seem to be slowed down in thinking.
______	______	40.	I have attacks of fear or panic and feel I have to do something to end it.
______	______	41.	I spend time sitting around or in bed.

TRUE	FALSE		
_____	_____	42.	Recently I've been thinking of ending it all.
_____	_____	43.	I am uneasy when I go out alone or stay home alone.
_____	_____	44.	My memory is impaired.
_____	_____	45.	I avoid going out alone or staying home alone.
_____	_____	46.	My movements are slowed down.
_____	_____	47.	I can't make up my mind.
_____	_____	48.	I have thoughts about killing myself.
_____	_____	49.	I am uneasy when in an enclosed space.
_____	_____	50.	I feel slowed down.
_____	_____	51.	I am discouraged about the future.
_____	_____	52.	I am uneasy when in crowds.
_____	_____	53.	I have lost interest in work.
_____	_____	54.	I avoid being in crowds.
_____	_____	55.	I can't concentrate on what people are saying.
_____	_____	56.	I get attacks of sudden fear or panic.
_____	_____	57.	I feel worthless.
_____	_____	58.	I have little interest in movies or T.V.
_____	_____	59.	I spend almost no time at recreation.
_____	_____	60.	I avoid being in an enclosed space.
_____	_____	61.	I feel ill at ease with people in general.
_____	_____	62.	My future is bleak.
_____	_____	63.	I continually feel afraid of things.
_____	_____	64.	I get angry with myself.
_____	_____	65.	I have a diminished appetite.
_____	_____	66.	I feel slowed down in my thinking.

Source: Fazio, A. F. *A Concurrent Validation Study of the NCHS' General Well-Being Schedule.* (Vital and Health Statistics: Series 2, Data Evaluation and Methods Research; No. 73, DHEW Publication No. (HRA) 78-1347). Washington, D.C.: U.S. Government Printing Office, 1977.

SCORING

This scale contains two subscales: anxiety and depression. To score the anxiety subscale, add up the TRUE answers you recorded for the following items:

4, 9, 13, 16, 18, 22, 25, 27, 31, 34, 36, 40, 43, 45, 49, 52, 54, 56, 60, 61, and 63

To score the depression subscale, add up the TRUE answers you recorded for the following items:

1, 2, 3, 5, 6, 7, 8, 10, 11, 12, 14, 15, 17, 19, 20, 21, 23, 24, 26, 28, 29, 30, 32, 33, 35, 37, 38, 39, 41, 42, 44, 46, 47, 48, 50, 51, 53, 55, 57, 58, 59, 62, 64, 65, and 66

INTERPRETATION OF SCORES

This scale measures the amount of anxiety and depression you feel. Generally, the higher the scores, the more feelings of anxiety and depression you experience. For the anxiety subscale, scores of 11 and higher indicate you experience high levels of anxiety. For the depression subscale, scores of 23 and higher indicate you experience high levels of depression. Again, the higher the score, the more of these feelings you experience.

ACTIVITY

Avoiding life's stressors should not be your goal. Instead, you should be striving for an optimal level of stress such that life is interesting while not being overbearing. Stressors should add spice to life, not illness or other negative consequences. Stress should be growth-producing and encourage you to do your best, not create a threat that causes you to be dissatisfied with your life. To achieve these ends, you need to analyze the stressors you currently experience—both unusual ones and those that are routine—and then adjust your life so as to experience only an optimal level of stress. Keeping a stress diary will help. You can use the form below.

STRESS DIARY DAILY RECORDS

Stressors	Reactions		Means of Coping	Means of Coping Better
	Physical	Emotional		
1. Routine a.				
b.				
2. Unique a.				
b.				

Relaxation Techniques Tried	Effectiveness of Technique
1.	
2.	
3.	

Sensations:	
Body	Mind

Keep your diary for two to three weeks. To analyze your diary, answer the following questions and consider their implications for changes in your life so as to experience a more manageable level of stress.

1. What stressors do you frequently experience?

   ____

   Do you need or want to continue experiencing these stressors?

   ____

   If you do not, which routine stressors can you eliminate?

   ____

   How?

   ____

2. How does your *body* typically react to stressors?

   ____

   How does your *mind* typically react to stressors?

   ____

   Can your body's or mind's reactions to stress teach you ways to identify stress early in its progression so as to make it less harmful? How?

   ____

3. Are there any coping techniques that you use more than others?

   ____

   Do these techniques work for you or against you?

   ____

4. Are there any coping techniques that you believe would be helpful but don't use often enough?

   ____

   How can you get yourself to use these infrequently-used coping techniques more often?

   ____

5. Are any particular relaxation techniques more effective for you than others?

   ____

Are you experiencing difficulty in employing a relaxation technique? No time? No place? No quiet?

____

How can you better organize your life to obtain periods of relaxation?

____

6. Are there any *mind/body* sensations that you usually experience either preceding or following stressful events?

   ____

   Are there ways to prevent either emotional or bodily sensations developing from your stress?

   ____

Summarize what you will *DO* as a result of recording and analyzing your stress diary. Be as *specific* as you can. For example, rather than state that you will relax more, describe the time of day, place, and method of relaxation.

I will: ____

____

____

____

____

____

____

____

____

____

____

____

____

Section III

Life Satisfaction

Being satisfied with your life is important in terms of experiencing a manageable amount of stress. The scales in this section measure your general life satisfaction, as well as how satisfied you are with particular facets of your life.

1) INTRODUCTION

How Satisfied Are You with Your Overall Life?

How you feel about the satisfaction you derive from your life affects the degree of stress you experience. This scale measures your general level of satisfaction with your life.

SCALE: LIFE SATISFACTION INVENTORY

Listed below are several factors that might influence your overall life satisfaction. In the IMPORTANCE column, indicate how important each factor is to you by using the following scale:

1 = Unimportant
2 = Somewhat important
3 = Very important

In the SATISFACTION column, indicate how satisfied you are with each factor by using the following scale:

1 = Unsatisfied
2 = Somewhat satisfied
3 = Very satisfied

FACTOR	IMPORTANCE	SATISFACTION
Your health		
Your physical appearance		
Your occupation (e.g., job, school, homemaking, child raising)		
Your ability to deal with people		
Your relationships with friends		
Your relationships with family		
Your sexual relationships		
Your spiritual life		
Your ability to handle problems		
Your financial condition		
Your leisure activities (e.g., hobbies, volunteer work, exercise program)		
Your accomplishments		
Your overall adjustment to life		

Source: Centers for Disease Control. *An Evaluation Handbook for Health Education Programs in Stress Management.* Washington, D.C.: Department of Health and Human Services, 1983, pp. 83–85.

SCORING

Multiply the point value you assigned for each factor on the "Satisfaction" rating by the point value you assigned for its corresponding "Importance" rating. This gives you a "weighted rating." Next, add the point values of all the weighted ratings and divide this sum by the average "Importance" rating in all factors. The weighted "Satisfaction" score is computed by dividing this number by the number of weighted responses (13). The maximum score is 3.0.

INTERPRETATION OF SCORES

This scale measures how satisfied you are with your life. High scores indicate a high degree of life satisfaction, giving more weight to those factors you consider to be the most important.

2) INTRODUCTION

How Satisfied Are You with Particular Facets of Your Life?

To obtain a measure more specific to particular facets of your life and your satisfaction with them, complete the scale below.

SCALE: NIDA LIFE SATISFACTION QUESTIONNAIRE

Consider how things have been going for you during the last few weeks. Below is a list of things that can influence your happiness and satisfaction with life. Please read each item and indicate how you have felt about it over the last few weeks. Indicate whether you have felt terrible, unhappy, mostly dissatisfied, mixed, mostly satisfied, pleased, delighted. Circle one answer for each.

Over the last few weeks, how have you felt about:	Terrible	Unhappy	Mostly dis-satisfied	Mixed	Mostly satisfied	Pleased	Delighted
1. Your overall satisfaction with your work (including being a student or housewife)	1	2	3	4	5	6	7
2. The amount of income you have	1	2	3	4	5	6	7
3. The amount of pay you get for the amount of work you do	1	2	3	4	5	6	7

	Terrible	Unhappy	Mostly dis-satisfied	Mixed	Mostly satisfied	Pleased	Delighted
4. Your liking for the actual work itself that is involved in your job	1	2	3	4	5	6	7
5. The physical surroundings and working conditions in your job	1	2	3	4	5	6	7
6. The amount of job security you have	1	2	3	4	5	6	7
7. Your overall health	1	2	3	4	5	6	7
8. Your overall physical condition	1	2	3	4	5	6	7
9. The amount of time you have for doing things you want to do	1	2	3	4	5	6	7
10. The chances you have for recreation and just taking it easy	1	2	3	4	5	6	7
11. What you are accomplishing with your life	1	2	3	4	5	6	7
12. Your ability to change things around you that you don't like	1	2	3	4	5	6	7
13. How interesting your day to day life is	1	2	3	4	5	6	7
14. Your ability to satisfy and meet your needs	1	2	3	4	5	6	7

	Terrible	Unhappy	Mostly dis-satisfied	Mixed	Mostly satisfied	Pleased	Delighted
15. The fullness and completeness of your love/sex life	1	2	3	4	5	6	7
16. Your ability to handle your emotions and feelings	1	2	3	4	5	6	7
17. Your religious life	1	2	3	4	5	6	7
18. The enjoyment you experience when you are around other people	1	2	3	4	5	6	7
19. How honest and sincere other people are with you	1	2	3	4	5	6	7
20. Your ability to gain cooperation from other persons	1	2	3	4	5	6	7
21. Your general enjoyment of life	1	2	3	4	5	6	7
22. Your sensitivity to other persons' feelings	1	2	3	4	5	6	7
23. Your standard of living: the things you have such as housing, car, furniture, recreation, etc.	1	2	3	4	5	6	7
24. How consistent and understand-able your world seems to be	1	2	3	4	5	6	7
25. The degree of love and accep-tance you feel from others	1	2	3	4	5	6	7
26. How happy you are	1	2	3	4	5	6	7

	Terrible	Unhappy	Mostly dis-satisfied	Mixed	Mostly satisfied	Pleased	Delighted
27. Your independence and freedom: the chance to do what you want to do	1	2	3	4	5	6	7
28. How you have handled problems that have come up	1	2	3	4	5	6	7
29. How much fun you are having	1	2	3	4	5	6	7
30. Your ability to take it when things get tough	1	2	3	4	5	6	7
31. The amount of intimacy and warmth in your life	1	2	3	4	5	6	7
32. The respect you get from others	1	2	3	4	5	6	7
33. Your ability to adjust to changes that come along	1	2	3	4	5	6	7
34. Your ability to get along with other people	1	2	3	4	5	6	7
35. The amount of friendship and love in your life	1	2	3	4	5	6	7
36. Your own family life	1	2	3	4	5	6	7
37. Your close relatives: parents, brothers, sisters, in-laws, etc.	1	2	3	4	5	6	7
38. The things you do and the times you have with friends	1	2	3	4	5	6	7

	Terrible	Unhappy	Mostly dis-satisfied	Mixed	Mostly satisfied	Pleased	Delighted
39. The standards and values in today's society	1	2	3	4	5	6	7
40. Your prospects for a good life in the future	1	2	3	4	5	6	7
41. Your success in getting ahead in the world	1	2	3	4	5	6	7
42. Your ability to concentrate	1	2	3	4	5	6	7
43. Your ability to get things done efficiently	1	2	3	4	5	6	7
44. Your ability to express your ideas to others	1	2	3	4	5	6	7
45. Your ability to share your feelings with persons who are close to you	1	2	3	4	5	6	7
46. Your ability to think things through and come up with good answers	1	2	3	4	5	6	7

Source: U.S. Department of Health and Human Services and National Institute on Drug Abuse. *Research Issue 28. Assessing Marijuana Consequences: Selected Questionnaire Items.* (DHHS Publication No. (ADM) 81-1150). Washington, D.C.: U.S. Government Printing Office, 1981.

SCORING

Add up your circled responses and divide by 46.

INTERPRETATION OF SCORES

This scale measures how satisfied you are with your various facets of your life. High scores indicate a high degree of life satisfaction. The average range of scores is 5.02 to 8.11, with the average score being 6.26. If you scored lower than 5.02, you indicated dissatisfaction with various facets of your life. If you scored above 8.11, you indicated satisfaction with many aspects of your life. Look at those items in which you responded with a 4 or less. Those are the facets of your life with which you are particularly dissatisfied.

ACTIVITY

Check the items on the *NIDA Life Satisfaction Questionnaire* to which you responded with a 1 or 2; that is, those items about which you feel either "Terrible" or "Unhappy". These are the items you need to work on changing if you expect to be more satisfied with your life. A good way to begin is to develop a contract with yourself, witnessed by someone else who you think will be supportive, to make the necessary change. You can use the contract that is below.

First you need to consider appropriate rewards and punishments for being able to successfully make the change you will soon identify or not being able to make that change. List these now:

REWARDS	PUNISHMENTS
1. ______________	1. ______________
2. ______________	2. ______________
3. ______________	3. ______________
4. ______________	4. ______________
5. ______________	5. ______________

Next, identify a supportive person you think can help you to make this change. Then complete this contract:

CONTRACT

I ______________________________ desire to improve ____________________
(your name)

because ____.
(the reason)

I have decided I intend to ____
(your target behavior)

by __________________________________. If I achieve this goal, I will reward
(date)

myself by ______________________________________. If I do not achieve my
(the reward)

goal, I will punish myself by ____.
(the punishment)

____
(Your signature) **(Today's date)**

____
(Witness signature) **(Today's date)**

Researchers have found contracts to be very effective in helping people make changes. You, too, can be successful and your life, thereby, more satisfying.

Section IV

Stress Knowledge

This section measures how much you know about stress and how much you know about how to manage stress effectively. If you don't know enough about stress and its causes, nor about the best ways to manage the stress you experience, you are more likely to have that stress develop into negative consequences. Such consequences can include threats to your health (for example, hypertension, heart disease, or headaches), difficulty concentrating on your job or school work, or impatience and tension that interfere with your interpersonal relationships.

1) INTRODUCTION

How Much Do You Know About Stress and Its Effects?

How much do you know about stress? Its causes? Its effects? This scale will help you determine your level of stress knowledge.

SCALE: FACTS ABOUT STRESS

This test consists of twenty statements about stress. Some of the statements are true and some are false. If you think a statement is true, put a check in the column labeled TRUE. If you think a statement is false, put a check in the column labeled FALSE.

TRUE	FALSE		
_____	_____	1.	People react to psychosocial stressors.
_____	_____	2.	Constant arousal due to stress can cause a person's blood pressure to remain at a low level.
_____	_____	3.	Stress due to overload can result from demands that occur at home.
_____	_____	4.	An individual who is adjusting to many life changes in a short period of time is less likely than usual to become ill.
_____	_____	5.	Thinking about an unpleasant event is never as stressful as actually experiencing the event.
_____	_____	6.	Thinking of oneself as useless and powerless can increase one's stress level.
_____	_____	7.	The most stressful situations are usually those over which people feel they have a great deal of control.
_____	_____	8.	Stress may decrease the body's ability to defend itself against disease.
_____	_____	9.	Severe stress may cause people to have accidents.
_____	_____	10.	One of the most common traits of the Type A personality is doing only one thing at a time.
_____	_____	11.	Excessive stress probably decreases the rate at which one's body uses up Vitamin C.
_____	_____	12.	A person under stress may feel confused.
_____	_____	13.	Overload occurs when people are able to meet the demands which are placed on them.
_____	_____	14.	A person under stress is often able to perform tasks better than usual.

TRUE FALSE

_____ _____ 15. Some degree of stress is necessary for life.

_____ _____ 16. Stress can lead to the failure of organ systems in the body.

_____ _____ 17. Too much stimulation is always more stressful than too little.

_____ _____ 18. High blood pressure can injure the heart even though there are no obvious symptoms.

_____ _____ 19. The stress produced by a situation depends more on the situation itself than on the person's perception of the situation.

_____ _____ 20. The Type A personality is associated with heart disease.

SCORING

Assign yourself one point for each of the following responses:

ITEM	ANSWER	ITEM	ANSWER
1	T	11	F
2	F	12	T
3	T	13	F
4	F	14	F
5	F	15	T
6	T	16	T
7	F	17	F
8	T	18	T
9	T	19	F
10	F	20	T

INTERPRETATION OF SCORES

This scale measures how much you know about stress and its effects. The higher the score, the more you know about stress. If you scored lower than 11, you should participate in activities to learn more about stress such as reading a book on stress or enrolling in a workshop or course concerned with stress.

Source: Centers for Disease Control. *An Evaluation Handbook for Health Education Programs in Stress Management.* Washington, D.C.: Department of Health and Human Services, 1983, pp. 89–92.

2) INTRODUCTION

How Much Do You Know About How to Manage Stress Effectively?

Knowing about stress and its effects is not sufficient for managing the stress you experience. This scale measures your specific knowledge of effective means for managing stress.

SCALE: COPING WITH STRESS

This test consists of twenty statements about stress. Some of the statements are true and some are false. If you think a statement is true, put a check in the column labeled TRUE. If you think a statement is false, put a check in the column labeled FALSE.

TRUE	FALSE		
_____	_____	1.	Imagining heaviness and warmth in one's body parts is an autogenic training technique.
_____	_____	2.	An individual should consume more caffeine during stressful times.
_____	_____	3.	Competitive physical activity is an effective stress management technique.
_____	_____	4.	Involvement in the pleasure of physical activity leads to feelings of well-being.
_____	_____	5.	Breaking down complicated tasks into smaller parts can reduce stress.
_____	_____	6.	Stress can be reduced by avoiding routines whenever possible.
_____	_____	7.	When undergoing important life changes, stress can be reduced by increasing the number of other changes that are made.
_____	_____	8.	Heartbeat can be monitored by biofeedback.
_____	_____	9.	Individuals should not try to change their relation to stressors.

TRUE FALSE

_____ _____ 10. Sitting comfortably helps to quiet one's internal environment.

_____ _____ 11. Autogenic training is an effective technique for relieving vascular problems associated with stress.

_____ _____ 12. Anticipating periods of boredom and planning activities for those periods can reduce stress.

_____ _____ 13. When using physical exercise as a stress management technique, one should try to exert oneself as much as possible.

_____ _____ 14. In autogenic training, an individual attempts to eliminate the physical sensations that are associated with relaxation.

_____ _____ 15. Becoming less competitive with oneself and others is an effective way to reduce Type A behavior.

_____ _____ 16. Delegating authority and responsibility to others will have no effect on one's stress.

_____ _____ 17. To be effective, relaxation must be used at the same time and place each time it is done.

_____ _____ 18. Being in a place away from other people helps to quiet one's external environment.

_____ _____ 19. Focusing on one's positive characteristics improves a person's self-concept.

_____ _____ 20. Increased muscle activity is a characteristic of relaxation.

Source: Centers for Disease Control. *An Evaluation Handbook for Health Education Programs in Stress Management.* Washington, D.C.: Department of Health and Human Services, 1983, pp. 97–100.

SCORING

Assign yourself one point for each of the following responses:

ITEM	ANSWER	ITEM	ANSWER
1	T	11	T
2	F	12	T
3	F	13	F
4	T	14	F
5	T	15	T
6	F	16	F
7	F	17	F
8	T	18	T
9	F	19	T
10	T	20	F

INTERPRETATION OF SCORES

This scale measures how much you know about how to effectively manage stress. The higher the score, the more you know about effectively managing stress. If you scored lower than 11, you should participate in activities to learn more about managing stress such as reading a book on stress management or enrolling in a workshop or course concerned with stress management.

ACTIVITY

The best ways to increase your knowledge of stress-related information are immersing yourself in reading about stress, attending stress management workshops, or enrolling in stress management courses at a local college or university. As an alternative, you might want to consider the purchase of audiotapes or videotapes that concern themselves with some aspect of stress or stress management. A list of such tapes appears below; as does a listing of selected books that pertain to stress and/or stress management. As you sort through these materials, consider identifying at least one method you will use to:

1. Change your *life* to eliminate a stressor (such as driving in on a less crowded road)
2. Change your *perception* of a stressor so you consider it less distressing (such as focusing on the good in a situation)
3. Manage your *emotions* to a stressor (such as meditate)
4. *Use* the built-up by-products of stress (such as exercise)

STRESS MANAGEMENT AUDIO AND VIDEOTAPES

AUDIOTAPES:

"A Guide To Happiness." Psychology Today Tapes, Dept. 964, Box 059073, Brooklyn, New York 11205-9061

"A Six-Second Technique To Control Stress." Psychology Today Tapes, Dept. 964, Box 059073, Brooklyn, New York 11205-9061

"Beating The Blues." American Health Products, Dept. A894, Box 11271, Des Moines, Iowa 50340

"Cognitive Control Cassette Tapes." New Harbinger Publications, 5674 Shattuck Avenue, Oakland, California 94609

"Conquer The Fear Of Public Speaking." Psychology Today Tapes, Dept. 964, Box 059073, Brooklyn, New York 11205-9061

"Deep Relaxation." Psychology Today Tapes, Dept. 964, Box 059073, Brooklyn, New York 11205-9061

"Effective Self-Assertion." Psychology Today Tapes, Dept. 964, Box 059073, Brooklyn, New York 11205-9061

"Exercises For Mind Expansion." Psychology Today Tapes, Dept. 964, Box 059073, Brooklyn, New York 11205-9061

"Getting Rid Of Your Fears." Psychology Today Tapes, Dept. 964, Box 059073, Brooklyn, New York 11205-9061

"How To Build Self-Esteem." Psychology Today Tapes, Dept. 964, Box 059073, Brooklyn, New York 11205-9061

"How To Stop Worrying and Start Living." Psychology Today Tapes, Dept. 964, Box 059073, Brooklyn, New York 11205-9061

"Hypnosis Tapes." New Harbinger Publications, 5674 Shattuck Avenue, Oakland, California 94609

"Learn To Relax: A 14 Day Program." Coulee Press, P.O. Box 1744, LaCrosse, Wisconsin 54602-1744

"Letting Go Of Stress." Source Cassettes, 945 Evelyn Street, Menlo Park, California 94025

"Maintaining Self-Esteem." Psychology Today Tapes, Dept. 964, Box 059073, Brooklyn, New York 11205-9061

"Meditation: A Sensible Guide To A Timeless Discipline." Research Press, Box 3177, Dept. K, Champaign, Illinois 61821-9988

"Meditation—An Instructional Cassette." Psychology Today Tapes, Dept. 964, Box 059073, Brooklyn, New York 11205-9061

"Mental Imagery: Techniques And Exercises." Psychology Today Tapes, Dept. 964, Box 059073, Brooklyn, New York 11205-9061

"Mental Imagery: Your Hidden Potential." Psychology Today Tapes, Dept. 964, Box 059073, Brooklyn, New York 11205-9061

"Natural Ocean Soundtrack." Route 8, Box 78, High Point, North Carolina 27260

"Nobody Is Perfect." Psychology Today Tapes, Dept. 964, Box 059073, Brooklyn, New York 11205-9061

"Overcoming Shyness." Psychology Today Tapes, Dept. 964, Box 059073, Brooklyn, New York 11205-9061

"Peak Performance." Psychology Today Tapes, Dept. 964, Box 059073, Brooklyn, New York 11205-9061

"Progressive Relaxation." Psychology Today Tapes, Dept. 964, Box 059073, Brooklyn, New York 11205-9061

"Progressive Relaxation Training." Psychology Today Tapes, Dept. 964, Box 059073, Brooklyn, New York 11205-9061

"Relaxation & Stress Reduction Cassette Tapes." New Harbinger Publications, 5674 Shattuck Avenue, Oakland, California 94609

"Relaxation Dynamics." Research Press, Box 3177, Dept. K, Champaign, Illinois 61821-9988

"Release Shoulder Tension." Kareena, c/o Yoga To Conga Drums, 1055 Pratt #3, Chicago, Illinois 60626

"Self-Relaxation Training." Research Press, Box 3177, Dept. K, Champaign, Illinois 61821-9988

"Ten-Minute Stress Manager." Source Cassettes, 945 Evelyn Street, Menlo Park, California 94025

"The Power of Self-Esteem." Audio-Forum, Dept. 542, Guilford, Connecticut 06437

"The Relaxed Body Cassette I For Muscle Relaxation." American Health Products, Dept. A90214, Box 11271, Des Moines, Iowa 50340

"The Relaxed Body Cassette II For Mental Relaxation." American Health Products, Dept. A90214, Box 11271, Des Moines, Iowa 50340

"The Self-Esteem Tapes." The Self-Esteem Tapes, Dept. A, 600 W. Grand, Suite 106, Hot Springs, Arizona 71901

"Transforming Stress Into Power." HEALTH EDCO, P.O. Box 21207, Waco, Texas 76702-1207

"Two Techniques For Treating Stress Disorders." Psychology Today Tapes, Dept. 964, Box 059073, Brooklyn, New York 11205-9061

"Understanding And Coping With Anxiety." Psychology Today Tapes, Dept. 964, Box 059073, Brooklyn, New York 11205-9061

"Visualization: Accessing The Higher Self." Psychology Today Tapes, Dept. 964, Box 059073, Brooklyn, New York 11205-9061

VIDEOTAPES:

"Attacking Anxiety." Veritas Programming, Ltd., Order Center, 175 Fifth Avenue, Suite 2548, New York, New York 10010

"Coping: Ways To Handle Stress I." Queue, Inc., 562 Boston Avenue, Room S, Bridgeport, Connecticut 06610

"Coping: Ways To Handle Stress II." Queue, Inc., 562 Boston Avenue, Room S, Bridgeport, Connecticut 06610

"Fitness: Getting It All Back." American Health Products, Dept. A90214, Box 11271, Des Moines, Iowa 50340

"Male Stress Syndrome." Films For The Humanities And Sciences, Inc., Box 2053, Princeton, New Jersey 08543

"Managing Stress." Films For The Humanities And Sciences, Inc., Box 2053, Princeton, New Jersey 08543

"Managing Stress, Anxiety And Frustration." Human Relations Media, Room HC 123, 175 Tompkins Avenue, Pleasantville, New York 10570-9973

"Massage Your Mate." Ozman, Inc., 496-A Hudson Street, #K-17, New York 10004

"Our Nation Under Stress." Films For The Humanities And Sciences, Inc., Box 2053, Princeton, New Jersey 08543

"Phobias." Films For The Humanities And Sciences, Inc., Box 2053, Princeton, New Jersey 08543

"Progressive Relaxation Training." Research Press, Box 3177, Dept. R, Champaign, Illinois 61821

"Stress: A Personal Challenge." Coronet/MTI Film & Video, 108 Wilmot Road, Deerfield, Illinois 60015

"Stress And Immune Function." Films For The Humanities And Sciences, Inc., Box 2053, Princeton, New Jersey 08543

"Stressbreak." Source Cassettes, 945 Evelyn Street, Menlo Park, California 94025

"Stress In The Later Years." Kent State University, Audio Visual Services, Kent, Ohio 44242

"Stress, Is Your Lifestyle Killing You." Kent State University, Audio Visual Services, Kent, Ohio 44242

"Stress Management." Great Performance, Inc., 700 N. Green, Chicago, Illinois 60622

"Stress: You Can Live With It." Coronet/MTI Film & Video, 108 Wilmot Road, Deerfield, Illinois 60015

"Teens Dealing With Stress." Queue, Inc., 562 Boston Avenue, Room S, Bridgeport, Connecticut 06610

"The Relaxed Body Video." American Health Products, Dept. A90214, Box 11271, Des Moines, Iowa 50340

"The Stress Test." Kent State University, Audio Visual Services, Kent, Ohio 44242

"The Time Bomb Within." Coronet/MTI Film & Video, 108 Wilmot Road, Deerfield, Illinois 60015

"Time Management." Wisconsin Clearinghouse, University of Wisconsin–Madison, Dept. CF, P.O. Box 1468, Madison, Wisconsin 53701

"Transforming Stress Into Power." HEALTH EDCO, P.O. Box 21207, Waco, Texas 76702-1207

"What The World Dishes Out." Coronet/MTI Film & Video, 108 Wilmot Road, Deerfield, Illinois 60015

"What You Bring On Yourself." Coronet/MTI Film & Video, 108 Wilmot Road, Deerfield, Illinois 60015

"Women And Stress." Films For The Humanities And Sciences, Inc., Box 2053, Princeton, New Jersey 08543

"Yoga: Volume I—Beginners." Rudra Press, P.O. Box 1973-A, Cambridge, Massachusetts 02238

"Yoga: Volume II—Intermediates." Rudra Press, P.O. Box 1973-A, Cambridge, Massachusetts 02238

BOOKS:

Allen, Roger J. *Human Stress: Its Nature and Control.* Minneapolis, MN: Burgess, 1983.

Benson, Herbert. *The Relaxation Response.* New York: Avon Books, 1985.

Charlesworth, Edward A. and Nathan, Ronald G. *Stress Management: A Comprehensive Guide to Wellness.* Houston, TX: Biobehavioral Publishers, 1982.

Friedman, Meyer and Rosenman, Ray H. *Type A Behavior and Your Heart.* Greenwich, CT: Fawcett, 1974.

Girdano, Daniel A., Everly, George S., and Dusek, Dorothy E. *Controlling Stress and Tension.* Englewood Cliffs, NJ: Prentice Hall, 1990.

Greenberg, Jerrold S. *Comprehensive Stress Management.* Dubuque, IA: Wm. C. Brown, 1990.

Greenberg, Jerrold S. *Coping With Stress: A Practical Guide.* Dubuque, IA: Wm. C. Brown, 1990.

Woolfolk, R. and Lehrer, P. (eds.). *Principles and Practices of Stress Management.* New York: Guilford Press, 1984.

Section V

Techniques for Responding Appropriately to Stress

This section not only measures your knowledge of effective means of managing stress, but also how effective you would actually be in managing particular stressful situations.

1) INTRODUCTION

How Effective Would You Be in Responding to Stressful Situations?

Using the scale on the next page, you can determine whether your responses to specific stressful situations would be appropriate. If not, the scale helps you determine whether your responses would be unhealthy, a direct violation of appropriate response, a denial, or outright ineffective.

SCALE: APPROPRIATE RESPONSES TO STRESS

This test presents descriptions of individuals who are in stressful situations. These people want to reduce their stress. Read each item. Circle the letter of the appropriate action for the person to take to reduce the stress. If there is no appropriate choice presented, circle Choice D, "None of the above."

1. Valerie has just been promoted to a new job in a different city. An appropriate way for Valerie to reduce her stress would be to:

   A. change her hairstyle and way of dressing to reflect her new image.
   B. take on as much work as she can to keep herself busy.
   C. establish a suitable schedule soon after she arrives.
   D. None of the above.

2. John is in a noisy office and is trying to concentrate on his work. An appropriate way for John to reduce his stress would be to:

   A. skip lunch and work during lunch hour when the office is quieter.
   B. rearrange the books and papers on his desk.
   C. wear more comfortable clothes to work.
   D. None of the above.

3. Bruce is worried that he will fail his history test, even though he has studied hard for it. An appropriate way for Bruce to reduce his stress would be to:

   A. stay up late the night before the test in order to study more.
   B. think about how angry his parents will be if he fails the test.
   C. go out and take a bicycle ride.
   D. None of the above.

4. Arthur is very busy typing when a co-worker asks Arthur to help her with her typing. Arthur is a bit annoyed by her request. An appropriate way for Arthur to reduce his stress would be to:

   A. help her with her typing but explain that he won't do it again.
   B. explain that he can't do her typing and concentrate on finishing his own work.
   C. pretend that his co-worker's request doesn't bother him and continue working.
   D. None of the above.

5. Paul has been told that there is no chance that he can pitch for his baseball team because the owner's son will be taking his place. An appropriate way for Paul to reduce his stress would be to:

   A. look into pitching for another team.
   B. get to know the other members of the team better.
   C. tell the owner that he insists on being able to pitch for the team, no matter what.
   D. None of the above.

6. Nancy drives home on a busy, crowded freeway. An appropriate way for Nancy to reduce her stress would be to:

   A. drive with the car windows open slightly.
   B. make sure that she takes the same route home whenever possible.
   C. drink a cup of coffee as she drives.
   D. None of the above.

7. Gary is concerned that the quality of his work is not good enough, even though all of the people he works with tell him he's doing a good job. An appropriate way for Gary to reduce his stress would be to:

   A. spend more time trying to improve the quality of his work.
   B. plan to have a few beers with his co-workers every day after work.
   C. spend more time focusing on the positive qualities of his work.
   D. None of the above.

8. Leslie has just recently married and moved to a new city. An appropriate way for Leslie to reduce her stress would be to:

   A. try to change some of her old habits.
   B. set aside some time each day to relax.
   C. take a vacation with her husband.
   D. None of the above.

9. Sharon works on an assembly line where she watches metal fittings go by all day long. An appropriate way for Sharon to reduce her stress would be to:

   A. bring in a soft cushion for her chair.
   B. ask her boss if she can listen to a radio as she works.
   C. see if she can work through lunch so that she can finish her work as quickly as possible.
   D. None of the above.

10. Karen had been planning on taking a week off from work. Now her boss tells Karen that it is impossible for her to have the vacation time she had planned. An appropriate way for Karen to reduce her stress would be to:

    A. threaten to switch jobs unless she can take her vacation as planned.
    B. act as if she didn't want the time off that much anyway.
    C. tell her boss that she's disappointed and ask if she can take the time off next month.
    D. None of the above.

11. Phyllis has four final exams and only two days left to study for them. An appropriate way for Phyllis to reduce her stress would be to:

    A. take her mind off her own tests by helping a friend study.
    B. pick the hardest course and study for that exam only.
    C. set up a schedule so that she has some time to study for each test.
    D. None of the above.

12. Gwen wants to be president of a local club but has been told that she doesn't have the organizational ability. An appropriate way for Gwen to reduce her stress would be to:

    A. stop attending club meetings.
    B. take a business class to improve her skills.
    C. tell the club members that she doesn't really want to be president.
    D. None of the above.

13. Gregg lives across from an all night gas station and is disturbed by the noise from the cars. An appropriate way for Gregg to reduce his stress would be to:

    A. play loud music to block out the noise.
    B. take a sleeping pill to help get to sleep.
    C. give all of his business to another gas station.
    D. None of the above.

14. Stanley is surrounded by people at a very crowded party. An appropriate way for Stanley to reduce his stress would be to:

    A. stay in the middle of the crowd.
    B. have several extra glasses of wine in order to relax.
    C. Loosen his tie so that he will feel more comfortable.
    D. None of the above.

15. Joyce must speak to a large group of people and keeps thinking about the time she was giving a speech in front of her class and forgot what she was to say. An appropriate way for Joyce to reduce her stress would be to:

    A. set aside some time before the speech to relax.
    B. remember as many details as she can about her previous experience giving a speech.
    C. keep her hands busy while she gives the speech.
    D. None of the above.

SCORING

Assign yourself one point for each of the following responses:

1. C	9. B
2. D	10. C
3. C	11. C
4. B	12. B
5. A	13. D
6. D	14. D
7. C	15. A
8. B	

Source: Centers for Disease Control. *An Evaluation Handbook for Health Education Programs in Stress Management.* Washington, D.C.: Department of Health and Human Services, 1983, pp. 105–112.

INTERPRETATION OF SCORES

This scale measures how effective you would be in responding to stressful situations. Using the key below, you can evaluate your incorrect answers as being either:

1. *Unhealthy*—a response that is unhealthy.
2. *Direct Violation*—a response that is in direct violation of the appropriate responses to stress.
3. *Denial*—a response that denies the stress or the problem producing the stress.
4. *Ineffective*—a response that is related to the situation but is ineffective in reducing stress. It is neither unhealthy, nor in direct violation, nor denial.
5. *None of the Above*—a response that indicates there is no correct answer when there *is* a correct answer.

INCORRECT ANSWER CHOICE ANALYSIS

	Unhealthy	Direct Violation	Denial	Ineffective	None of the Above
1.	—	A	—	B	D
2.	A	—	—	B,C	—
3.	A	B	—	—	D
4.	—	A	C	—	D
5.	—	C	—	B	D
6.	C	—	—	A,B	—
7.	B	—	—	A	D
8.	—	A,C	—	—	D
9.	C	—	—	A	D
10.	—	A	B	—	D
11.	—	A	—	B	D
12.	—	—	C	A	D
13.	B	A	—	C	—
14.	B	A	—	C	—
15.	—	B	—	C	D

ACTIVITY

One very appropriate response to stress that has been demonstrated effective is called *Selective Awareness.* Selective awareness is learning to perceive life changes and other stressors as less distressing by attending to their *positive* aspects and de-emphasizing their *negative* ones. We all are free to choose what to think, although most of us don't exercise this control of our thoughts but allow them to ride the high seas rudderless. To complicate matters, we have been taught to be critical rather than supportive, focusing on the bad rather than the good. To help you learn to focus on the positive aspects of situations and people, rephrase the following situations so the focus is upon their positive components:

1. Waiting in a long line to attend a movie

 ____

 ____

2. Being stuck in bumper-to-bumper traffic

 ____

 ____

3. Having to make a presentation before a group of people

 ____

 ____

4. Being rejected from something because you're too old

 ____

 ____

5. Having a relationship break up

 ____

 ____

Right now there are situations in your life that are causing you a great deal of stress. You may not like where you live, or whom you're living with, or the work you're doing. You may not feel you have enough time to yourself or for leisure activities. You may not like the way you look. You may be in poor health. You may be alone. Some of these stressors you may be able to change; some you will not be able to change. You now know, however, that you can become selectively aware of their positive components while de-emphasizing (though not denying) their disturbing features. Below, list these stressors, and list the positive aspects of each upon which you will choose to focus:

SELECTIVE AWARENESS: Stressors and Their Positive Aspects:

1. Stressor: ______________________________

   Positive Aspect: ______________________________

2. Stressor: ______________________________

   Positive Aspect: ______________________________

3. Stressor: ______________________________

   Positive Aspect: ______________________________

Why not go even further? Each time you do something that works out well, keep the memory of that with you. Tell others how proud of yourself you are. Pat yourself on the back. Take time just before bed (or some other convenient time of day) to recall all the good things about that day. Don't be like some of your friends who can't sleep because they still feel embarrassed about something they did that day or worried about something over which they have no control. In the words of a best seller of several years ago, "Be your own best friend." Revel in your good points and the glory of your day.

Section VI

Using Systematic Decision-Making Skills

There is a body of knowledge related to the use of a systematic method of arriving at decisions. The use of such a method would result in more effective decisions than might otherwise be the case. The result would be less stress from making poor decisions. This section speaks to your knowledge of, your belief in the value of, and your intention to use systematic decision-making skills.

1) INTRODUCTION

What Do You Know About Systematic Decision Making?

You can't use systematic decision making unless you are knowledgeable about that technique. This scale measures your knowledge of systematic decision making.

Dr. Brooking

SCALE: DECISION MAKING

> This test presents descriptions of people who are trying to make decisions that may affect their health or the health of others.
>
> Read each item. Circle the letter of the *next* step that the person should take in order to be making decisions using a *systematic approach.*

1. Katherine is slightly overweight and wants to go on a diet. Although she has tried to diet before, she has never had much success with the diets she has chosen. Now Katherine realizes she must choose a diet that isn't too difficult so that she will stick with it.

   She discusses her desire to find a suitable diet with one of her close friends. Together they identify several different diet plans that may be useful for Katherine. Katherine thinks about how she feels about going on a diet. She then discusses the different diets with her family doctor who points out the positive and negative features of each. They also discuss what Katherine will have to do in order to stick to each diet plan.

   What is the best thing for Katherine to do *next* in order to use the systematic decision-making approach?

   A. Discuss the different diets with another friend.
   B. Select one of the diets.
   C. Have her doctor select one of the diets for her.
   D. Realize that she must choose a suitable diet.

2. William started smoking many years ago, before the dangers of cigarette smoking were known. Now he recognizes that his cigarette smoking is bad for his health. Although William knows that it might be difficult, he wants to quit smoking. Some of his friends who used to smoke have already quit. William is sure that there are many different ways to stop smoking. He wants to choose the way that is right for him.

   What is the best thing for William to do *next* in order to use the systematic decision-making approach?

   A. Call a smoking clinic to find out about its program.
   B. Decide how he will quit smoking.
   C. Make a list of all the possible ways he can stop smoking.
   D. Think of one way he can stop smoking.

3. Cindy has been invited to a party where other people will probably be smoking marijuana. Although Cindy has never smoked marijuana, she is curious about it. She realizes that she must decide what she will do if someone at the party offers her marijuana. Cindy thinks about what she might do. After Cindy goes to the library and reads some books on marijuana, she decides not to smoke at the party. While at the party, Cindy is offered marijuana several times but turns down the offers.

   What is the best thing for Cindy to do *next* in order to use the systematic decision-making approach?

   A. Talk to her friends about smoking marijuana.
   B. Read more books about marijuana.
   C. Avoid the people who offered her marijuana at the party.
   D. Consider whether she's happy about her decision.

4. Martin enjoys being active and tries to exercise on the weekends. He would like to exercise every day after work. Some of his co-workers go to a gym near his office. His wife jogs every evening at the local park.

   What is the best thing for Martin to do *next* in order to use the systematic decision-making approach?

   A. Think of one type of exercise he enjoys.
   B. Start to jog after work.
   C. Realize he must choose a regular exercise program.
   D. Talk to his co-workers about the gym.

5. Phil works in a very busy office. He has a great deal of work to do and sometimes he is unable to complete it on time. Phil knows that he is under stress at work and he wants to find a good way to reduce it. He discusses his problem with some of his friends. He then makes a list of all the ways that he knows of to reduce stress at work.

   What is the best thing for Phil to do *next* in order to use the systematic decision-making approach?

   A. Get information about his ideas from the company doctor.
   B. Select one of the ideas on his list.
   C. Ask his doctor to choose a good way for him to reduce the stress at work.
   D. Realize that he must find an appropriate way to reduce the stress at work.

6. Mary wants to take her son to be immunized at a local clinic. The clinic is very busy. Her child can have an appointment only on a day when Mary has an important business meeting.

   Mary already has made a doctor's appointment in two months for her child's routine checkup. She realizes that she must decide whether to take her child to the clinic or wait and have her child immunized at the doctor's office. Mary thinks about her possibilities. She calls the doctor and the clinic to find out if it is safe to wait.

   What is the best thing for Mary to do *next* in order to use the systematic decision-making approach?

   A. Think about the possible choices available to her.
   B. Decide what to do about immunizing her son.
   C. Be aware that she must make a decision about her son's immunization.
   D. Complain to the clinic's staff that they aren't flexible enough.

7. Phyllis works for the Westinger Company. For the last few months Phyllis has been swimming during lunch hour. She enjoys the swim and is pleased with the improvement in her health and appearance.

   Her boss now wants Phyllis to attend board meetings that are held every Monday, Wednesday, and Friday at lunch time. She tells Phyllis that attending the meetings will be important for her growth in the company.

   What is the best thing for Phyllis to do *next* in order to use the systematic decision-making approach?

   A. Choose between swimming and attending the board meetings.
   B. Try to convince her boss that she doesn't need to attend board meetings.
   C. Talk to her boss about the decision she must make.
   D. Realize that she must decide between swimming and attending the meetings.

8. Debbie has diabetes. She keeps her diabetes under control by eating a special diet.

   Debbie's new boss is having a dessert party in a few days and Debbie is invited. All of the guests are supposed to bring their favorite dessert. Debbie shouldn't eat sweets and desserts, but she doesn't want to offend her boss by turning down the invitation. Debbie realizes that she must decide whether or not to go to the party. She thinks about the options that she has and discusses them with a friend who also has diabetes. She calls her doctor to ask his advice about eating sweets just one time. She also thinks about whether she would be able to resist eating anything at the party if she went.

What is the best thing for Debbie to do *next* in order to use the systematic decision-making approach?

A. Decide whether to go to the party.
B. Have her doctor decide whether she should go to the party.
C. Sign up for a special baking class for people with diabetes.
D. Make a list of her possible choices.

9. Gary visits the doctor once a year for a checkup. At one checkup the doctor discovers that Gary's blood pressure is slightly higher than it should be. He wants Gary to use deep relaxation because that may lower Gary's blood pressure. If it doesn't, Gary may have to take a special medicine.

   Gary recognizes that he must decide whether or not to use deep relaxation. He wants to follow his doctor's advice, but Gary understands that using relaxation may not lower his blood pressure. Gary makes a list of possible choices and the consequences.

   What is the best thing for Gary to do *next* in order to use the systematic decision-making approach?

   A. Decide whether or not he will follow his doctor's advice.
   B. Talk with a friend who has high blood pressure about the effects of relaxation.
   C. Realize that he has a decision to make about using relaxation.
   D. Discuss the possibilities with his doctor.

10. Diane is going to make some big changes in her life soon. She will be moving to a new city to start school and she is nervous about it.

    Diane has heard that changes can cause stress, but that there are ways to reduce it. She wants to choose a way to reduce some of the stress she's feeling.

    What is the best thing for Diane to do *next* in order to use the systematic decision-making approach?

    A. Start a regular exercise program.
    B. Discuss with her family the possible ways she can reduce her stress.
    C. Decide on a way to relieve the stress she feels.
    D. Have the family doctor choose a way for her to reduce the stress.

11. Bob is quite heavy. He wants to lose weight and realizes that he must decide how he's going to do it. He discusses the situation with his wife. Together they realize that Bob will either have to go on a diet, start exercising regularly, or do both. Bob calls his doctor to get his advice. The doctor says that regular exercise may reduce Bob's appetite so that it will be easier to stay on a diet. The doctor suggests that Bob try to diet and exercise. Bob, however, doesn't enjoy exercising so he decides to go on a diet only.

Bob tries to diet for three weeks. He's unhappy because he's not losing much weight and is often hungry.

What is the best thing for Bob to do *next* in order to use the systematic decision-making approach?

A. Think about whether he is satisfied with his decision to lose weight by dieting.
B. Read books about weight loss.
C. Stay with his diet for at least another week.
D. Start a running program in order to follow his doctor's advice about exercising.

12. Joe drinks a great deal of alcohol. He always has many drinks after work. Lately he has been drinking when he gets up in the morning. He knows that he has a drinking problem.

What is the best thing for Joe to do *next* in order to use the systematic decision-making approach?

A. Enroll in an alcoholism treatment program.
B. Watch other people to see if they drink as much as he does.
C. Recognize that he must decide what to do about his drinking.
D. Realize that he will have to decide what changes to make in his life.

13. Margaret wants to stop smoking. She knows that there are many ways to quit and that she should choose the best way for her. She discusses the matter with a friend. They come up with several plans: (a) Margaret could stop smoking completely on a certain day, or (b) Margaret could slowly reduce the number of cigarettes she smokes each day until she gives them up completely. Margaret calls her doctor to ask her doctor's opinion. She also talks to other people who have already quit smoking.

Margaret decides to stop smoking gradually. At the start of every week she reduces the number of daily cigarettes she smokes by one. Unfortunately, Margaret isn't too happy with her program and she has trouble keeping track of the number of cigarettes she smokes.

What is the best thing for Margaret to do *next* in order to use the systematic decision-making approach?

A. Have her doctor choose a way for Margaret to stop smoking.
B. Think again about her decision to stop smoking gradually.
C. Stick with her decision regardless of how she feels about it.
D. Read some books about how to stop smoking.

14. Stan wants to get into good physical condition, even though he smokes and has not exercised in years. He is aware that there are many ways to exercise and that some ways are better than others. He wants to find an exercise program that will be comfortable and effective for him.

    Stan talks to some friends to find out what they do to get and stay in shape.

    What is the best thing for Stan to do *next* in order to use the systematic decision-making approach?

    A. Decide on an exercise program.
    B. Quit smoking before he starts an exercise program.
    C. Read some books about the different exercises he has heard about.
    D. Jog regularly because he enjoys being outside.

15. Tom has been on a low-salt, low-fat diet for several months. He is pleased with the diet, even though following it can be difficult. He does have to prepare most of his meals himself from fresh foods.

    Tom has been asked to go on vacation with some friends. He wants to go but he knows that he won't be able to prepare his own meals. If he goes, he may not be able to stay on his diet very well. Tom realizes that he has a decision to make about going with his friends.

    What is the best thing for Tom to do *next* in order to use the systematic decision-making approach?

    A. Decide not to go on vacation.
    B. Have his doctor decide if Tom should go with his friends.
    C. Think about whether his friends would mind if he didn't go.
    D. Consider the options available to him.

SCORING

Assign yourself one point for each of the following responses:

1. B
2. C
3. D
4. C
5. A
6. B
7. D
8. A
9. D
10. B
11. A
12. C
13. B
14. C
15. D

Source: Centers for Disease Control. *An Evaluation Handbook for Health Education Programs in Stress Management.* Washington, D.C.: Department of Health and Human Services, 1983, pp. 118–128.

INTERPRETATION OF SCORES

This scale measures how much you know about systematic decision-making. Using the key below, you can evaluate your incorrect answers as being either:

1. *Skipped Step*—a response that describes one of the decision-making steps that occurs after the correct step.
2. *Repeated Step*—a response that describes one of the decision-making steps that has already occurred.
3. *Ineffective Implementation of Correct Step*—a response that describes the correct decision-making step, but violates one or more of the step's effectiveness criteria.
4. *Ineffective Implementation of Incorrect Step*—a response that describes an incorrect decision-making step and violates one or more of the step's effectiveness criteria.
5. *Deflective Action*—a response that is unrelated to effective decision making and may deflect the decision maker from taking necessary action.

INCORRECT ANSWER CHOICE ANALYSIS

	Skipped Step	Repeated Step	Ineffective Implementation of Correct Step	Ineffective Implementation of Incorrect Step	Deflective Action
1.	—	A,D	C	—	—
2.	B	—	D	A	—
3.	—	A,B	—	—	C
4.	B,D	—	—	A	—
5.	B	D	—	C	—
6.	—	A,C	—	—	D
7.	A,C	—	—	—	B
8.	—	D	—	—	C
9.	A	C	B	—	—
10.	A,C	—	B	D	—
11.	—	B	C,D	—	—
12.	A	—	D	—	B
13.	—	D	C	A	—
14.	A,D	—	—	—	B
15.	A,C	—	—	B	—

2) INTRODUCTION

How Valuable Do You Believe Systematic Decision-Making Is In Arriving at Appropriate Decisions?

Just knowing about systematic decision-making is not enough. You need to believe it is valuable or else you will not bother to use it. This scale measures how valuable you believe systematic decision-making skills can be in arriving at appropriate decisions.

SCALE: IDEAS ABOUT SYSTEMATIC DECISION-MAKING

This survey is about making decisions systematically. Please respond to all the statements in the survey.

Read each statement. Decide the extent to which you agree with it. Circle the appropriate letter to the left of the statement. Use the following scale:

SA = Strongly Agree
A = Agree
U = Uncertain
D = Disagree
SD = Strongly Disagree

SA A U D SD 1. People who make decisions systematically reach better decisions than people who don't.
SA A U D SD 2. Systematic decision-making takes too much time.
SA A U D SD 3. People who use systematic decision-making have greater control over the events in their lives.
SA A U D SD 4. People make equally good decisions no matter how they arrive at them.
SA A U D SD 5. Systematic decision-making is too complicated.
SA A U D SD 6. It is worth the time to make decisions systematically.
SA A U D SD 7. A systematic decision-making process doesn't consider how people feel.
SA A U D SD 8. People who use systematic decision-making won't make hasty decisions that they will regret later.
SA A U D SD 9. Systematic decision-making is too intellectual.
SA A U D SD 10. Systematic decision-making helps people make the best choice when deciding important things in their lives.

SA A U D SD 11. Systematic decision-making only works when making decisions with a group of people.

SA A U D SD 12. Systematic decision-making is the best way to make decisions.

SA A U D SD 13. Systematic decision-making is easy when people learn how to use it.

SA A U D SD 14. Only logical people have the skills needed for systematic decision-making.

SA A U D SD 15. Systematic decision-making is not flexible enough.

SA A U D SD 16. The effort involved in making decisions systematically is well worth it.

SA A U D SD 17. It is too hard to get the information needed to make decisions systematically.

SA A U D SD 18. Systematic decision-making helps people think about their values when they make decisions.

SA A U D SD 19. People follow through with decisions they have made systematically.

SA A U D SD 20. People make their best decisions when they follow their first impulses.

Source: Centers for Disease Control. *An Evaluation Handbook for Health Education Programs in Stress Management.* Washington, D.C.: Department of Health and Human Services, 1983, pp. 213–216.

SCORING

Assign the following point values for each response.

	SA	A	U	D	SD
1.	5	4	3	2	1
2.	1	2	3	4	5
3.	5	4	3	2	1
4.	1	2	3	4	5
5.	1	2	3	4	5
6.	5	4	3	2	1
7.	1	2	3	4	5
8.	5	4	3	2	1
9.	1	2	3	4	5
10.	5	4	3	2	1
11.	1	2	3	4	5
12.	5	4	3	2	1
13.	5	4	3	2	1
14.	1	2	3	4	5
15.	1	2	3	4	5
16.	5	4	3	2	1
17.	1	2	3	4	5
18.	5	4	3	2	1
19.	5	4	3	2	1
20.	1	2	3	4	5

Next, divide the sum of your points by 20.

INTERPRETATION OF SCORES

This scale measures your belief in the utility of using systematic decision-making. The maximum score obtainable is 5. A score of 3.5 or higher indicates a belief that using systematic decision-making is useful. If you believe it is useful, you will be more apt to use systematic decision-making.

3) INTRODUCTION

How Strong Is Your Intention to Use Systematic Decision-Making Skills?

To determine whether you are likely to actually use systematic decision-making skills, you need to measure your intent to employ this technique when a decision is required. This scale measures your intention to actually use systematic decision-making when appropriate.

SCALE: WOULD YOU USE SYSTEMATIC DECISION-MAKING?

This survey describes situations in which people might use systematic decision making. Read each statement. Circle Yes or No to indicate whether you would use systematic decision making in the situation described in the item.

If you circle Yes, then use the Confidence Scale to show how certain you are that you would use systematic decision making in that situation.

The following examples show how the Confidence Scale is used.

	WOULD YOU USE SYSTEMATIC DECISION MAKING?	IF YES, HOW CERTAIN ARE YOU?
1. You are deciding on a career.	(YES) NO	90
2. You are choosing where to eat lunch.	(YES) NO	70
3. You are swerving to avoid a car accident.	YES (NO)	

Confidence Scale

10	20	30	40	50	60	70	80	90	100
Very Uncertain				Somewhat Certain					Very Certain

SITUATION	WOULD YOU USE SYSTEMATIC DECISION-MAKING?	IF YES, HOW CERTAIN ARE YOU?
1. You are deciding whether to start an exercise program.	YES/NO	________
2. You are choosing a diet.	YES/NO	________
3. You are being rushed by others to make a quick decision.	YES/NO	________
4. You are choosing an exercise program.	YES/NO	________
5. You are being urged by others to make a decision in their favor.	YES/NO	________
6. You are selecting a way to reduce your stress.	YES/NO	________
7. You are deciding whether to see a doctor.	YES/NO	________
8. You are making a decision and have many other things to do.	YES/NO	________
9. You are deciding whether to take vitamins.	YES/NO	________
10. You are deciding what to eat for dinner.	YES/NO	________
11. You are deciding whether to use a nonprescription drug.	YES/NO	________

SITUATION	WOULD YOU USE SYSTEMATIC DECISION-MAKING?	IF YES, HOW CERTAIN ARE YOU?
12. You are deciding whether to start a diet.	YES/NO	________
13. You are deciding what to do for a cold.	YES/NO	________
14. You are making a decision while you have many things on your mind.	YES/NO	________
15. You are deciding what to do to relax.	YES/NO	________

SCORING

Total all the confidence ratings made in conjunction with a "YES" response and divide this sum by 15. Confidence ratings made in conjunction with a "NO" response should be omitted from the analysis.

INTERPRETATION OF SCORES

The maximum score attainable of 100 represents your strong intention to use systematic decision-making in a variety of situations, along with a high level of confidence in that ability. Scores lower than 50 mean you are unsure that you will use systematic decision-making and that you can be effective in its use. Merely intending to use systematic decision-making is not good enough here. You need to be confident that you can use it well or it is likely that you won't try.

Source: Centers for Disease Control. *An Evaluation Handbook for Health Education Programs in Stress Management.* Washington, D.C.: Department of Health and Human Services, 1983, pp. 220–223.

ACTIVITY

Making decisions can and should be more systematic than is usually the case. If decisions were more systematic, better decisions would be made and the result would be less distress derived from poor decisions. This activity teaches one system for making decisions and encourages you to use this system for a decision you need to make.

The model of decision making we will use includes six steps:

1. *Perceive The Problem.* Recognizing that the problem exists is the first step in solving it.
2. *Define The Problem.* Narrow the scope of the problem so that it can be solved.
3. *Get Ideas About The Problem.* Generate as many possible solutions as can be thought up. Do not evaluate the solutions at this point. The idea is to accumulate as many as possible.
4. *Evaluate The Ideas.* Evaluate each of the ideas that have been generated in order to determine the relative merits of each alternative.
5. *Act.* Choose one alternative and put it into action.
6. *React.* Evaluate the action taken and determine whether it has been effective (if so, continue it) or ineffective (in which case, try to put another alternative into action).

To use this system, identify a decision you need to make and complete the form below:

DECISION-MAKING FORM

1. The decision I need to make is: ______________________________

   ____

2. More specifically, this problem entails: ______________________________

   ____

3. Possible solutions are: ______________________________

   a. ____

   b. ____

c. ______

d. ______

e. ______

4. The advantages of each possible solution are:

   a. ______

   b. ______

   c. ______

   d. ______

   e. ______

5. The disadvantages of each possible solution are:

   a. ______

   b. ______

   c. ______

   d. ______

   e. ______

6. The best possible solution is: ______

   ______

7. I will try this solution (when?): ______

8. After trying the solution, I found that:

   a. ______ It Worked

   b. ______ It Didn't Work

9. If the solution didn't work, I will next try: ______

   ______

Section VII

Effective Communication Techniques

To use communication to help cope with stress, you need to know both how to communicate your feelings of stress to other people, and how to communicate acceptance and understanding when other people share their stressful feelings with you. This section concerns these two communication skills.

1) INTRODUCTION

How Well Can You Communicate Your Feelings of Stress to Other People?

Research shows that if you can share your feelings of stress with other people—loved ones, friends, relatives, co-workers, and classmates—you will be less apt to suffer from the negative effects of that stress. This scale measures your skill in communicating your stressful feelings to others.

SCALE: COMMUNICATING ABOUT STRESS

This test presents descriptions of people who want to communicate their feelings about stress. They each have a message that they want to communicate to someone else.

Read each item. Then circle the letter of the choice that expresses the individual's message clearly and directly. If there is no clear and direct response given, circle choice D, "None of the above."

1. Michael wants to communicate to his friend that he gets nervous while driving through heavy traffic. The most clear and direct way for Michael to say this is:

   A. "I get really anxious when I have to drive in heavy traffic."
   B. "Everyone who drives in heavy traffic gets nervous."
   C. "I can't possibly drive home through this traffic without getting nervous."
   D. None of the above.

2. Martin wants to tell his son that he feels depressed about retiring from the company where he has worked for twenty years. The most clear and direct way for Martin to say this is:

   A. "You know how I feel about not working anymore."
   B. "I'll be retiring from the company soon."
   C. "I feel sad when I realize I won't be going into work anymore."
   D. None of the above.

3. Reggie wants to ask his wife to serve herbal tea instead of coffee at night to help him relax. The most clear and direct way for Reggie to say this is:

   A. "People can't relax if they are served coffee at night."
   B. "You're not being very sensitive to my needs if you continue to serve coffee at night."
   C. "I think it would help me relax if you would serve herb tea after dinner."
   D. None of the above.

4. Joyce wants to tell her husband that she feels happy about being able to keep her cool during an important job interview. The most clear and direct way for Joyce to say this is:

   A. "Now I'll never have to worry again about getting nervous when I'm in a tight spot."
   B. "You know what it means to me to have remained calm during the interview."
   C. "I had a good job interview today."
   D. None of the above.

5. Mark wants to tell his friend that he gets anxious when he has to wait in long lines at the bank or in the grocery store. The most clear and direct way for Mark to say this is:

   A. "You know how annoyed I get when I'm stuck in a long line."
   B. "I am sure everybody hates waiting in long lines."
   C. "You must not have much to do if waiting in long lines doesn't bother you."
   D. None of the above.

6. Janice has started to meditate every evening to help her manage her stress more effectively. She wants to ask her roommate not to interrupt her when she's meditating. The most clear and direct way for Janice to say this is:

   A. "It's not very considerate of you to interrupt me when I'm meditating."
   B. "Please help me out by leaving me alone sometimes."
   C. "Please help me manage my stress by not interrupting me while I meditate."
   D. None of the above.

7. Bruce wants to tell James, his co-worker, that he feels good about being able to stay calm during a very busy time at the office. The most clear and direct way for Bruce to say this is:

   A. "I feel good about work now."
   B. "I was able to keep my cool during that busy time here and I feel good about it."
   C. "You know how good it feels to keep your cool during difficult times here in the office."
   D. None of the above.

8. Gerald plans to jog in the morning before work as part of his stress management program. He wants to ask his wife to help him by making sure he doesn't oversleep in the morning. The most clear and direct way for Gerald to say this is:

   A. "Everyone needs help sticking to a stress management program, so please help me with mine."
   B. "Please help me with my stress management program by making sure I get up on time to go jogging."
   C. "If you really care about my health, you'll help me get up on time to go jogging in the morning."
   D. None of the above.

9. Jane gets nervous driving to work in traffic. She decides to reduce her stress by riding her bicycle to work instead of taking the car. She wants to tell her friend that she feels good about her decision. The most clear and direct way for Jane to say this is:

   A. "Everyone should ride a bicycle to work."
   B. "I feel great about riding my bike instead of driving to work."
   C. "You can imagine how good I feel riding my bike to work."
   D. None of the above.

10. Valerie wants to tell her family that she's nervous about moving away to a different city. The most clear and direct way for Valerie to say this is:

    A. "There's no way I'll ever feel good about moving."
    B. "You couldn't possibly understand how I feel about moving."
    C. "I feel anxious about moving to another city."
    D. None of the above.

11. Gregg drinks a great deal of coffee at work and notices that it makes him feel nervous. He wants to ask his co-worker to help him drink less coffee by keeping track of the amount of coffee he drinks. The most clear and direct way for Gregg to say this is:

    A. "Please help me drink less coffee because you know how nervous I get when I drink too much coffee."
    B. "Either you're going to keep track of how much coffee I drink or I'm going to be a nervous wreck."
    C. "Please help me drink less coffee."
    D. None of the above.

12. Gwen is trying to reduce the stress in her life by setting up a weekly time schedule. She wants to tell her friend Henry that she's very happy about how much calmer she feels since she has started using the schedule. The most clear and direct way for Gwen to say this is:

    A. "You can see how much my time schedule has helped me."
    B. "I feel very calm since I've started setting up weekly time schedules."
    C. "I think everyone should use a weekly time schedule."
    D. None of the above.

13. Sheila is trying to consume less sugar as part of her stress management program. She wants to ask her roommate not to offer her anything sweet to eat. The most clear and direct way for Sheila to say this is:

    A. "Please don't offer me anything sweet because I'm trying to eat less sugar."
    B. "You don't help me when you offer me sweet foods to eat."
    C. "Everyone finds cutting back on sugar difficult, so please help me try to do it."
    D. None of the above.

14. Victor wants to tell his wife that he feels very nervous every time he thinks about the examination that he must take in a few weeks. The most clear and direct way for Victor to say this is:

    A. "This test that I have to take is a pain."
    B. "I guess I'll always get nervous about examinations."
    C. "You can imagine how nervous I am about the examination."
    D. None of the above.

15. Donald wants to tell his family how good he feels since he's started practicing progressive relaxation everyday. The most clear and direct way for Donald to say this is:

    A. "You can tell how good I feel since I've started using progressive relaxation."
    B. "I feel great about practicing progressive relaxation every day."
    C. "You must be blind not to see how good I feel since I've started practicing relaxation."
    D. None of the above.

Source: Centers for Disease Control. *An Evaluation Handbook for Health Education Programs in Stress Management.* Washington, D.C.: Department of Health and Human Services, 1983, pp. 160–168.

SCORING

Assign yourself one point for each of the following responses:

1. A	9. B
2. C	10. C
3. C	11. D
4. D	12. B
5. D	13. A
6. C	14. D
7. B	15. B
8. B	

INTERPRETATION OF SCORES

This scale measures how well you can communicate your feelings of stress to other people. Using the key below, you can evaluate your incorrect answers as being either:

1. *Overgeneralized*—a response that extends a single experience to all experiences or always associates a particular behavior with certain circumstances.
2. *Crystal Ball*—a response in which the assumption is made that the receiver already knows the sender's feelings or the content of the message.
3. *Judgment*—a response that blames or criticizes.
4. *Incomplete*—a response that does not provide all the information needed to send a complete message.
5. *None of the Above*—a response that indicates there is no correct answer when there is a correct answer.

INCORRECT ANSWER CHOICE ANALYSIS

	Overgen-eralized	Crystal Ball	Judgment	Incomplete	None of the Above
1.	B,C	—	—	—	D
2.	—	A	—	B	D
3.	A	—	B	—	D
4.	A	B	—	C	—
5.	B	A	C	—	—
6.	—	—	A	B	D
7.	—	C	—	A	D
8.	A	—	C	—	D
9.	A	C	—	—	D
10.	A	—	B	—	D
11.	B	A	—	C	—
12.	C	A	—	—	D
13.	C	—	B	—	D
14.	B	C	—	A	—
15.	—	A	C	—	D

2) INTRODUCTION

How Well Can You Communicate Acceptance and Understanding When Other People Share Their Stressful Feelings with You?

Part of learning to communicate about stress is to learn how to present yourself as accepting and understanding of other people's attempts at sharing their stressful feelings with you. If you can't express acceptance and understanding, how can you expect other people will express acceptance and understanding when you share your feelings of stress with them? This scale measures your skill in communicating acceptance and understanding when other people share their stressful feelings with you.

SCALE: RESPONDING TO OTHERS ABOUT STRESS

> This test presents statements by individuals who want to communicate their feelings about stress. Read each statement. Then circle the letter of the response that best communicates acceptance and understanding of the message.

1. Bonnie: "I get very anxious when I have to drive to work in heavy traffic."

   The response that best communicates acceptance and understanding of Bonnie's situation is:

   A. "Try to drive to work earlier in order to miss some of the traffic."
   B. "There really is no reason to get so anxious about driving in heavy traffic."
   C. "You become very nervous when you drive to work in heavy traffic."
   D. "You should take the bus to work instead of driving in heavy traffic."

2. Gary: "I feel very nervous at the office when I have more work to do than I can keep up with."

   The response that best communicates acceptance and understanding of Gary's situation is:

   A. "You will have a heart attack if you let yourself get so nervous."
   B. "It sounds like you're pushing yourself too hard at the office."
   C. "You never seem nervous at the office to me."
   D. "You feel nervous when you can't keep up with all the work you have to do at the office."

3. Maggie: "I am proud of myself for practicing progressive relaxation every day."

   The response that best communicates acceptance and understanding of Maggie's situation is:

   A. "You feel good about yourself because you're sticking to your progressive relaxation schedule."
   B. "You'd sure be sorry if you didn't practice your relaxation skills every day."
   C. "You should practice relaxation in the morning so you'll feel calm all day long."
   D. "Try listening to soft music as you practice your relaxation skills."

4. Mike: "I feel terrific because I've cut down on the amount of coffee I drink."

   The response that best communicates acceptance and understanding of Mike's situation is:

   A. "You should drink herb tea instead of whatever coffee you still drink."
   B. "Drinking any coffee at all can make you very nervous."
   C. "You're feeling great because you're drinking less coffee."
   D. "If you still drink any coffee at all, that's too much."

5. Fred: "Could you please not disturb me when I'm practicing my relaxation skills?"

   The response that best communicates acceptance and understanding of Fred's situation is:

   A. "You should practice your relaxation skills when no one is around."
   B. "You want me to leave you alone while you're practicing your relaxation."
   C. "Relaxation skills are useless if they don't work when there are distractions around."
   D. "Try using ear plugs to block out noise while you are practicing."

6. Francis: "I've been a little depressed since I moved away from my family."

   The response that best communicates acceptance and understanding of Francis' situation is:

   A. "You're a little unhappy since you've left your family."
   B. "Perhaps you were too attached to your family."
   C. "You really have no reason to be depressed."
   D. "Why don't you call your family every week to stay in touch with them?"

7. Stuart: ''I feel great about swimming three times a week as part of my stress management program.''

   The response that best communicates acceptance and understanding of Stuart's situation is:

   A. ''Try swimming every day so that you'll feel even better.''
   B. ''You'll be sorry if you don't stick to that stress management program.''
   C. ''You don't need a stress management program.''
   D. ''You're happy because you're swimming regularly as a part of your stress management program.''

8. Doug: ''Would you help me manage my stress by encouraging me to make weekly time schedules?''

   The response that best communicates acceptance and understanding of Doug's situation is:

   A. ''You should rely on yourself only to manage your stress.''
   B. ''You want me to encourage you to use time schedules to manage your stress.''
   C. ''You must doubt your ability to manage stress if you need my encouragement.''
   D. ''You might be sorry if you depend on my encouragement to manage your stress.''

9. Sara: ''I've felt good since I started taking deep breaths whenever I am a little tense.''

   The response that best communicates acceptance and understanding of Sara's situation is:

   A. ''If you don't keep up deep breathing, you can end up just as nervous as you were.''
   B. ''Deep breaths help you relax and so you probably feel less stress.''
   C. ''You've started using deep breathing skills when you are tense and you feel good about that.''
   D. ''You might want to start exercising to help you reduce stress.''

10. Matthew: "I'm really starting to enjoy the jogging that was prescribed as part of my stress management program."

    The response that best communicates acceptance and understanding of Matthew's situation is:

    A. "You're beginning to enjoy jogging now."
    B. "As the jogging gets easier for you it also becomes more enjoyable."
    C. "Try jogging in the morning before you go to work."
    D. "You will have to continue to jog if you want to keep your stress level down."

11. Ellen: "Would you help me manage my stress by not offering me foods that contain a great deal of sugar?"

    The response that best communicates acceptance and understanding of Ellen's situation is:

    A. "You can eat some foods with sugar as long as you don't overdo it."
    B. "I'll be glad to help you but you shouldn't need me to help you watch what you eat."
    C. "It must be very hard to avoid sugar when people frequently offer you sweet foods."
    D. "You want me to help you avoid foods with sugar by not offering you any."

12. Ed: "I really feel anxious when I have to work in a noisy office."

    The response that best communicates acceptance and understanding of Ed's situation is:

    A. "There's no reason to let a little noise bother you."
    B. "Find the quietest area in the office and try to work there."
    C. "You get nervous when you have to work and the office is noisy."
    D. "Try to get used to the noise by taking deep breaths as soon as it starts to bother you."

13. Chris: "I feel a little embarrassed when I practice progressive relaxation at work."

    The response that best communicates acceptance and understanding of Chris' situation is:

    A. "I bet that you are worried about what your co-workers might think if they see you."
    B. "You're embarrassed when you practice your relaxation skills at work."
    C. "Think how nervous you'd feel if you didn't practice your relaxation skills at work."
    D. "Think of the good it does you instead of thinking about your embarrassment."

14. Julie: "I feel great because I'm changing my lifestyle to be simpler and less stressful."

    The response that best communicates acceptance and understanding of Julie's situation is:

    A. "I'm glad because you always had more things to do than you could do well."
    B. "You were headed for trouble if you didn't make your life less stressful."
    C. "You must have been under a lot of stress to make major changes in your lifestyle."
    D. "You are living a simpler, less stressful life and you feel good because of it."

15. Bill: "I'm proud that I've lowered by blood pressure by following a stress management program."

    The response that best communicates acceptance and understanding of Bill's situation is:

    A. "You should continue to follow your stress management program."
    B. "You're pleased that because of following your stress management program, your blood pressure is lower."
    C. "You'll be sorry if you don't continue to follow your stress management program."
    D. "Your blood pressure wasn't that high in the first place."

SCORING

Assign yourself one point for each of the following responses:

1.	C	9.	C
2.	D	10.	A
3.	A	11.	D
4.	C	12.	C
5.	B	13.	B
6.	A	14.	D
7.	D	15.	B
8.	B		

Source: Centers for Disease Control. *An Evaluation Handbook for Health Education Programs in Stress Management.* Washington, D.C.: Department of Health and Human Services, 1983, pp. 174–182.

INTERPRETATION OF SCORES

This scale measures how well you can communicate acceptance and understanding when other people share their stressful feelings with you. Using the key below, you can evaluate your incorrect answers as being either:

1. *Directing*—a response that tells or suggests to the message sender what to do.
2. *Warning*—a response that warns a message sender what might happen.
3. *Criticizing/Disagreeing*—a response that criticizes or disagrees with the message sender.
4. *Diagnosing*—a response that suggests an explanation for the message sender's statement.

INCORRECT ANSWER CHOICE ANALYSIS

	Directing	Warning	Criticizing/ Disagreeing	Diagnosing
1.	B,D	—	B	—
2.	—	A	C	B
3.	C,D	B	—	—
4.	A	B	D	—
5.	A,D	—	C	—
6.	D	—	C	B
7.	A	B	C	—
8.	A	D	—	C
9.	D	A	—	B
10.	C	D	—	B
11.	—	—	A,D	C
12.	B,D	—	A	—
13.	D	C	—	A
14.	—	B	A	C
15.	A	C	D	—

ACTIVITY

In order to be able to communicate well, you need to acquire certain skills. This activity helps you learn how to employ reflective listening, acknowledge feelings expressed to you, and use "I" statements. *Reflective Listening:* To demonstrate that you are listening to someone, you can paraphrase what he or she has said and what you think that person is feeling. Paraphrasing uses other words than those said which have the same meaning. For example, if you paraphrased the statement, "What a rotten day!" you might say, "It seems that your day was really horrendous." In this way, the other person will know that you listened. Practice this reflective listening by rephrasing the following statements:

1. I'm really feeling stressed out.

 ____

2. My instructors are so unsympathetic that I don't know if I'll do well in school this semester.

 ____

3. Cindy and I are not getting along very well lately.

 ____

One way you might have reflected these statements back to the person communicating them is:

1. So much is happening that you obviously feel uptight and tense.
2. It sounds like you're worried you won't get good grades this semester and that you can't expect any help from your teachers. That must be very frustrating and scary.
3. You're worried about the future of your relationship with Cindy and what you can do to improve it, aren't you?

Acknowledging Feelings: When someone communicates feelings to you, it is best to acknowledge those feelings and accept them. For example, if I said, "I'm really upset that you would do such a thing," you might respond, "You seem disappointed and angry with me." In this way, you are recognizing that I have certain feelings and accepting that they exist. That doesn't mean that you think those feelings are warranted, only that you acknowledge their existence. Try responding to the following feeling statements with an acknowledgment of them:

1. I get depressed every time I think of the death of my father.

   ____

2. I'll never be able to get up in front of the class and give that report with everyone looking at me.

   ____

3. I don't have very much confidence in myself.

   ____

One way you might have made an acknowledging response to these statements is:

1. Your father's death has affected you greatly, even to this day. I imagine I'll react the same way when my father dies.
2. Your feelings of anxiety and self-doubt are quite understandable. I experience these same feelings when I have to speak in front of a bunch of people.
3. It must feel terrible not trusting your abilities. I feel for you.

"I" Statements: When you communicate by talking about the other person's behavior, that person is liable to feel defensive. One way to prevent that reaction is to use "I" statements. For example, if you want to complain about my not spending enough time with you, you could say, "You don't spend enough time with me and I'm really upset about that." Then, I have to defend not spending enough time with you. Instead, you could say, "I get upset when people I care for don't spend enough time with me." I'll know what you mean but will be more likely to consider that statement as a piece of information you're providing rather than a specific complaint requiring a justification of my behavior to you. Reword the following statements so they are "I" statements:

1. You require too much work in this class and I don't think that's fair.

   ____

2. I don't get the sense that you care about me because you are always looking away when I speak to you.

   ____

3. You aren't even sensitive enough to put your arm around me when I'm opening up to you.

   ____

One way you might have reworded these statements is:

1. When so much work is required that it doesn't seem it can ever be done in the time allotted, I feel as though I'm being treated unfairly.
2. When someone I'm speaking to doesn't look directly at me, I get the feeling that person doesn't care about me.
3. When I open up to someone and that person doesn't express enough concern to make physical contact with me—such as putting an arm around me—I don't feel as though that person is very sensitive or even cares very much about me.

Section VIII

Positive Outlook on Life

It is important to maintain a positive outlook on life in order to be satisfied and happy. Without such an outlook, you may experience a great deal of stress from everyday hassles, as well as extraordinary events, that will be extremely stressful and unmanageable. Optimism will go a long way to help you cope with the stress in your life. This section concerns your outlook on life.

1) INTRODUCTION

How Optimistic Are You About Your Future?

Feeling positive about what the future holds can be protection against the harmful effects of stress. This scale measures your outlook (your optimism) by asking you to guess at the satisfaction you will experience in the quality of your life for the short-term (one year) and for the long-term (ten years).

SCALE: HOW WILL YOU FEEL?

Listed below are several factors that might influence your expectations about the quality of your life in the near and distant future.

In the IMPORTANCE column, indicate how important each factor is to you by using the following scale:

1 = Unimportant
2 = Somewhat important
3 = Very important

In the EXPECTED SATISFACTION IN ONE YEAR column, indicate how satisfied you expect to be with each factor *one year from now.*

In the EXPECTED SATISFACTION IN TEN YEARS column, indicate how satisfied you expect to be with each factor *ten years from now.*

For both EXPECTED SATISFACTION columns, use the following scale:

1 = Expect to be *unsatisfied*
2 = Expect to be *somewhat satisfied*
3 = Expect to be *very satisfied*

FACTOR	IMPORTANCE	EXPECTED SATISFACTION IN ONE YEAR	EXPECTED SATISFACTION IN TEN YEARS
Your health			
Your physical appearance			
Your occupation (e.g., job, school, homemaking, child-raising)			
Your ability to deal with people			
Your relationships with friends			
Your relationships with family			
Your sexual relationships			
Your spiritual life			
Your ability to handle problems			
Your financial condition			
Your leisure activities (e.g., hobbies, volunteer work, exercise program)			
Your accomplishments			
Your overall adjustment to life			

SCORING

Multiply the point value of each "Expected Satisfaction" rating by the point value of its corresponding "Importance" rating. The total "Importance-Weighted Expected Satisfaction" score for one year and for ten years is computed by adding the point values for all of the "Expected Satisfaction" ratings for that column, dividing this sum by the average "Importance" rating of all factors and dividing this number by the number of weighted responses. For either the one year or ten year period, the maximum score attainable is 3.0.

Separate scores for each time period can also be combined to obtain an "Overall Importance-Weighted Expected Satisfaction" index which incorporates expectations for one and ten year periods. An "Overall Importance-Weighted

---

Source: Centers for Disease Control. *An Evaluation Handbook for Health Education Programs in Stress Management.* Washington, D.C.: Department of Health and Human Services, 1983, pp. 183–186.

Expected Satisfaction" score is computed by dividing the sum of the weighted "Expectation Satisfaction" scores for each time period by 2. The maximum "Overall Importance-Weighted Expected Satisfaction" score attainable is 3.0.

INTERPRETATION OF SCORES

This scale measures how optimistic you are about your future life satisfaction for two time periods: one year from now and ten years from now. High scores for the separate time periods or their combination indicate highly optimistic expectations for life satisfaction, giving more weight to those factors considered by you to be most important. If your scores are below 2.0, that indicates you are not optimistic that your future will be sufficiently satisfying for you.

ACTIVITY

You have more control over your future than you might think. You can arrange your life to be more satisfying if you exercise that control. For example, you can spend time with people that you enjoy being with and can hang out at places where you derive satisfaction. Then, you will be more optimistic about your short-range and long-range future. The following activity will help you organize your life to do that.

Fill in the following People/Places Grid. In Quadrant I list five people you like, in Quadrant II list five people you dislike, in Quadrant III list five places you like, and in Quadrant IV list five places you dislike.

PEOPLE/PLACES GRID

People Liked: (I)	People Disliked: (II)
1.	1.
2.	2.
3.	3.
4.	4.
5.	5.
I	II
III	IV
Places Liked:	Places Disliked:
1.	1.
2.	2.
3.	3.
4.	4.
5.	5.

Now, on a separate sheet of paper, you are going to identify the characteristics of people you like and dislike and places you like and dislike.

Take Quadrant I first: What do the people that you like have in common? Perhaps they have a good sense of humor or are caring and considerate. Perhaps they enjoy sports or are hard workers. On your separate sheet of paper, list these characteristics. Don't limit yourself to characteristics that *all* of them possess, but rather characteristics that describe *many* (at least three of the five) people you've listed.

Let's look at Quadrant II now: What do the people that you dislike have in common? Perhaps they are noisy or are poor listeners. Perhaps they are too serious or are selfish. On your separate sheet of paper, list these characteristics. Again, don't limit yourself to characteristics that *all* of them possess, but rather characteristics that describe at least three of the five people you've listed.

We'll do the same for Quadrant III: What is it that places you like have in common? Perhaps they are busy and noisy or all full of activity. Perhaps they are quiet and conducive to conversation. Perhaps they have warm climates or an ocean or other body of water nearby. On your separate sheet of paper, list these characteristics. Again, don't limit yourself to characteristics that *all* of them possess, but rather characteristics that describe at least three of the five places you've listed.

Lastly, do the same for Quadrant IV: What is it that places you dislike have in common? Perhaps they are too quiet or lack interesting things to do. Perhaps they are in cold, windy climates or too remote from a large city. Perhaps they are too "high brow" and not "earthy" enough for you. Once again, don't limit yourself to characteristics that *all* of them possess, but rather characteristics that describe at least three of the five places you've listed.

Now that you've identified characteristics descriptive of people and places you like and dislike, you can use this information to make your life more satisfying and less stressful. For instance, make a plan to spend time with the *kind of people* you like and limit relationships with the *kind of people* you dislike. This seems obvious. However, we don't always use this strategy when meeting *new* people, and don't really understand why it is that other relationships of ours are either so enjoyable or so unpleasant.

Increase the likelihood of being more satisfied with your life and less stressful by filling in the information below:

PEOPLE AND PLACES ANALYSIS

Who are the people you want to spend more time with?

______________________	______________________
______________________	______________________
______________________	______________________

Who are the people you want to limit time with?

______________________	______________________
______________________	______________________
______________________	______________________

Where do you want to spend more time?

______________________	______________________
______________________	______________________
______________________	______________________

Where do you want to limit time?

______________________	______________________
______________________	______________________
______________________	______________________

There are other ways to use the information you've generated about the people and places you like and dislike. For instance, ask yourself the following questions:

1. What would happen if I took the people I like to the places I like?

   Would I have a GREAT time? Or would I be unable to focus my attention on the people because of the characteristics of the place? Or would I be unable to focus my attention on the place because of the characteristics of the people?

2. What would happen if I took the people I like to the places I dislike?

   Would I like the people less? Or would I like the places more? Would the places interfere with my relationships with the people, or would the people be so enjoyable to be with that the negative characteristics of the places would be more tolerable?

3. What would happen if I took the people I dislike to the places I like?

   Would I like the people more? Or would I like the places less because of sharing them with people around whom I feel uncomfortable? Could I ever enjoy these places again or would they be forever ruined by the memory of having shared them with people I dislike? How would I feel if people I like found out I shared the places I like with people I dislike?

In essence, you have just asked yourself whether you are a *people* person or a *places* person. Are people more important to you than where you are, or is your environment more important to you than the people in it? There is no right or wrong answer. People just differ in this perspective. The point is that you should know which you find more important so you can better organize your life to be consistent with this perspective.

Section IX

Intention to Use Stress Management Techniques

This book will not be very useful unless you actually intend to, and eventually do, use the stress management techniques presented here or in other sources to which you have been referred. A prior question, however, is your belief regarding how effective you believe you can be in managing the stress in your life. This section, therefore, concerns both your perception of your self-efficacy in managing stress and your intention to actually employ stress management techniques and strategies.

1) INTRODUCTION

How Effective Do You Think You Can Be In Managing Stress?

Although you may believe people can manage stress, you may not be sure of your ability to manage the stress you experience. This scale measures your stress-related self-efficacy; that is, your perception of your ability to manage the stress you personally experience.

SCALE: KEEPING YOUR COOL

This survey describes various times when people might feel stress. Read each statement. Circle YES or NO to show if you would feel stress at that time.

If you circle YES, then use the Confidence Scale to show how certain you are that you *could manage the stress* from that situation. Stress management requires that you try to reduce excess pressures in order to increase your ability to lead a productive and satisfying life.

The following examples show how the Confidence Scale is used.

SITUATION	MIGHT YOU FEEL STRESS?	IF YES, HOW CERTAIN ARE YOU THAT YOU COULD MANAGE THE STRESS?
1. You have just spent the worst day of your life.	(YES)/NO	20
2. You have just spent a typical day.	(YES)/NO	70
3. You have just spent the most relaxing day of your life.	YES/(NO)	____

Confidence Scale

0 10 20 30 40 50 60 70 80 90 100

Very Uncertain — Somewhat Certain — Very Certain

SITUATION	MIGHT YOU FEEL STRESS?	IF YES, HOW CERTAIN ARE YOU THAT YOU COULD MANAGE THE STRESS?
1. You are trying to concentrate but you are constantly being interrupted.	YES/NO	____

SITUATION	MIGHT YOU FEEL STRESS?	IF YES, HOW CERTAIN ARE YOU THAT YOU COULD MANAGE THE STRESS?
2. You have to do a very boring task.	YES/NO	________
3. You have been thinking about someone who hurt you in the past.	YES/NO	________
4. You have a neighbor who plays loud music all the time.	YES/NO	________
5. You have several things to finish in a very short time.	YES/NO	________
6. You are home by yourself and feel lonely.	YES/NO	________
7. You are in a crowded bus and can't get to the exit in time for your stop.	YES/NO	________
8. You keep thinking about an unpleasant experience.	YES/NO	________
9. You have taken on more than you can do.	YES/NO	________
10. You are waiting on the street for someone to pick you up, and you are getting cold.	YES/NO	________

SITUATION	MIGHT YOU FEEL STRESS?	IF YES, HOW CERTAIN ARE YOU THAT YOU COULD MANAGE THE STRESS?
11. Although you have plenty of time, you are worried that you will be late for an important appointment.	YES/NO	________
12. Your closest friend has left town and you feel alone.	YES/NO	________
13. You are in a room that is extremely hot.	YES/NO	________
14. You must buy a gift for someone and the stores are closing.	YES/NO	________
15. You saw someone being robbed and keep imagining that it could happen to you.	YES/NO	________
16. You have to wait for a delivery and you have nothing to do.	YES/NO	________
17. Your friends keep asking you to do things you don't have time to do.	YES/NO	________
18. You must get a prescription filled and you can't find a drug store that is open.	YES/NO	________

SITUATION	MIGHT YOU FEEL STRESS?	IF YES, HOW CERTAIN ARE YOU THAT YOU COULD MANAGE THE STRESS?
19. You spend a good deal of time in a place that is very noisy.	YES/NO	______
20. No matter how hard you have tried, you haven't been able to finish all your work.	YES/NO	______

SCORING

Compute the sum of the confidence ratings made in conjunction with a "YES" response. Divide this sum by the number of "YES" responses. The maximum score obtainable is 100. Omit from the scoring any confidence ratings for items to which you responded "NO."

INTERPRETATION OF SCORES

This scale measures how confident you are that you can manage stressful situations when they occur. High scores (over 50) indicate you are confident that you can manage the stress that you will experience. Low scores (below 50) indicate you do not believe you will be very successful managing the stressful events that you may encounter.

Source: Centers for Disease Control. *An Evaluation Handbook for Health Education Programs in Stress Management.* Washington, D.C.: Department of Health and Human Services, 1983, pp. 190–194.

2) INTRODUCTION

How Intent Are You on Using Stress Management Techniques?

We conclude this book by giving you a chance to determine how intent you are on employing stress management techniques to help you cope with the stress of your life. This scale measures the degree to which you are committed to use stress management strategies.

SCALE: WILL YOU MANAGE STRESS?

This survey describes things that people might do to manage stress. Read each statement. Circle YES or NO to show if you intend to do what is described in the item.

If you circle YES, then use the Strength of Intention Scale to show how strong your intention is to do what is described.

The following examples show how the Strength of Intention Scale is used.

	DO YOU INTEND TO DO THIS?	IF YES, HOW STRONG IS YOUR INTENTION?
1. Eat something every day.	(YES)/NO	90
2. Go to a store this week.	(YES)/NO	70
3. Try to swim across an ocean.	YES/(NO)	____

Strength of Intention Scale

10	20	30	40	50	60	70	80	90	100
Very Weak									Very Strong

	DO YOU INTEND TO DO THIS?	IF YES, HOW STRONG IS YOUR INTENTION?
1. Find alternatives for goals you have been unable to reach.	YES/NO	________
2. Stay away from crowded places if they make you nervous.	YES/NO	________
3. Do the most important things first when you have too many things to do.	YES/NO	________
4. Find interesting things to do when you are bored.	YES/NO	________
5. Use earplugs when you are in very noisy places.	YES/NO	________
6. Avoid unnecessary changes when you have many other things to do.	YES/NO	________
7. Look at the positive things in yourself and your life.		
8. Take one thing at a time.	YES/NO	________
9. Get plenty of sleep every night.	YES/NO	________
10. Talk about your problems with friends or family.	YES/NO	________
11. Talk about your problems with the people who are involved in them.	YES/NO	________
12. Balance work with relaxing activities.	YES/NO	________

	DO YOU INTEND TO DO THIS?	IF YES, HOW STRONG IS YOUR INTENTION?
13. Use relaxation techniques.	YES/NO	________
14. Get regular exercise.	YES/NO	________
15. Avoid large amounts of caffeine.	YES/NO	________
16. Try to identify what is causing you stress.	YES/NO	________
17. Accept realistic goals for yourself and others.	YES/NO	________
18. Avoid having many big changes come at the same time.	YES/NO	________
19. Get professional help if you feel too much stress.	YES/NO	________
20. Accept what you cannot change.	YES/NO	________

SCORING

Total all the strength ratings made in conjunction with a "YES" response and divide this sum by 20 (the total number of items in this scale). Strength ratings made in conjunction with a "NO" response should be eliminated from the scoring analysis. The maximum score attainable is 100.

Source: Centers for Disease Control. *An Evaluation Handbook for Health Education Programs in Stress Management.* Washington, D.C.: Department of Health and Human Services, 1983, pp. 200–203.

INTERPRETATION OF SCORES

This scale measures how intent you are on using stress management techniques. High scores (over 50) indicate you strongly intend to employ a number of stress management techniques to manage the stress in your life. Low scores (below 50) indicate you are generally not intent on using a variety of stress management techniques to manage stress.

ACTIVITY

For you to actually use stress management techniques, you need to believe they will be effective. The following activity is but one that has some real practical utility.

To begin, list as many of your worries as you can identify. *BIG* worries and *small* worries. Serious worries and insignificant ones. List every single worry you can; *as many* as you can. *DO THAT NOW* before proceeding with this activity.

Now let's make more sense of the worries you listed. Place your worries on the following *Worry Grid* according to the following instructions:

If the worry involves something you *Can Control* and which is *Important* to you, list it in Quadrant I.

If the worry involves something you *Cannot Control* but which is *Important* to you, list it in Quadrant II.

If the worry involves something you *Can Control* but which is *Not Important* to you, list it in Quadrant III.

If the worry involves something you *Cannot Control* and which is *Not Important* to you, list it in Quadrant IV.

DO NOT PROCEED UNTIL YOU HAVE LISTED EACH AND EVERY WORRY SOMEPLACE IN THE WORRY GRID.

WORRY GRID

	Can Control	Cannot Control
Important	I	II
Not Important	III	IV

Once you listed all your worries on the Worry Grid, you need to check your work **CAREFULLY.**

Look at Quadrant I: Are there any worries listed here which are either really beyond your control or are really not very important? If so, delete that worry from Quadrant I and move it to the appropriate quadrant in the grid.

What you are now left with in Quadrant I are only those worries which are both important to you and over which you can exercise some control. Those are the **ONLY** worries you need to focus on. Here's why:

Left in Quadrant II are worries which, while important to you, can be little influenced by anything you do since you cannot exercise any control over them. If there's nothing you can do, why worry? The worry serves no useful purpose and only makes you unhappy and distressed. It's like worrying about flying on an airplane. Once in the air, unless you know how to fly a plane, worrying does you no good. At that point, worrying only makes you nervous, increases your blood pressure and the serum cholesterol roaming about in your blood, and has the potential to make you ill. Why worry about things that you have no influence over? What will be, will be. Place an X through Quadrant II.

Left in Quadrant III are worries which you can exercise some control over but which are not very important to you. For these worries, the potential to get ill and elicit a stress response is not worth it. You yourself have said these things are not very important. If not very important, why worry about them. They're not worth the time or the energy and effort that worrying about them requires. What makes most sense in relation to these worries is to ignore them. They're just not important enough to waste your time, energy, and effort on them. Place an X through Quadrant III.

Left in Quadrant IV are worries which you both cannot exercise any control over and which are not very important to you. These worries are almost irrelevant. Who cares about them; or, rather, who should care about them? Certainly not you! You don't consider them important and, even if you did, there's nothing you can do about them anyhow! Let's not even spend any more time on these. Place an X through Quadrant IV immediately.

Remaining are the Quadrant I worries. As we've said before, these worries are both important to you and there **IS** something you can do to influence events relative to these worries. Now that you've isolated Quadrant I worries from the others—others which aren't important anyhow, or if they are, can't be influenced—you can focus upon what **IS** really important and about which you **CAN** do something. The other worries are no longer clouding the picture.

Next, you need to choose each of the Quadrant I worries separately and devise a plan to exert the control you stated you had. This will increase the likelihood they will turn out the way you desire. There are no *guarantees* that what you are worried about will turn out the way you'd like it to. However, you can increase the probabilities that it will work out as you choose. At least you know that doing something is better than doing nothing!

Spend a few moments to determine how best to exert the control you stated you had over Quadrant I worries.

Now go about putting your plan into operation.

You'll see how much better you'll feel and how much less worried you'll become.